Workbook

EXPLORING German

THIRD EDITION

Joan G. Sheeran

Consultants
Judith Gray Myrth
Wolfgang S. Kraft

EMC Publishing

ST. PAUL • LOS ANGELES • INDIANAPOLIS

Editorial Director: Alejandro Vargas B.
Developmental Editor: Wolfgang S. Kraft
Production Editor: Amy McGuire
Production Specialist: Parkwood Composition
Cover Designer: Leslie Anderson

Care has been taken to verify the accuracy of information presented in this book. However, the authors, editors, and publisher cannot accept responsibility for Web, e-mail, newsgroup, or chat room subject matter or content, or for consequences from application of the information in this book, and make no warranty, expressed or implied, with respect to its content.

We have made every effort to trace the ownership of all copyrighted material and to secure permission from copyright holders. In the event of any question arising as to the use of any material, we will be pleased to make the necessary corrections in future printings. Thanks are due to the aforementioned authors, publishers and agents for permission to use the materials indicated.

ISBN 978-0-82193-486-9

875 Montreal Way
St. Paul, MN 55102
E-mail: educate@emcp.com
Web site: www.emcp.com

Printed in the United States of America

19 18 17 5 6 7 8 9 10

Name: ______________________ Datum: ______________

UNIT 1

A **Wie heißt du?** ***(How good are you with names? Can you identify each of the following?)***

1. girl's name starting with C: ______________
2. boy's name starting with N: ______________
3. girl's version of the name Peter: ______________
4. boy's version of the name Heike: ______________
5. girl's version of the name Leon: ______________
6. boy's version of the name Andrea: ______________
7. girl's name starting with A: ______________
8. boy's name starting with D: ______________
9. girl's name staring with M: ______________
10. boy's name starting with F: ______________

B **In the list below are the German names of girls and boys. Do you know them well enough to sort them out? Write the names for *Mädchen* and the names for *Jungen* in the appropriate column.**

Simon Heike Elisabeth Stefan Johanna Jochen Beate Günther Eberhard Nele Karsten Gabriele

Mädchen	Jungen
______________	______________
______________	______________
______________	______________
______________	______________
______________	______________
______________	______________

Name: ______________________ Datum: ______________________

C Match the situation with the appropriate response.

_____ 1. You say good-bye to a friend.

_____ 2. You ask a new student what his/her name is.

_____ 3. You say "hi" to a girl.

_____ 4. You make a mistake and feel bad about it.

_____ 5. You wish a friend well on her English test.

_____ 6. You say good night to your parents.

A. Viel Glück!

B. Es tut mir leid.

C. Wie heißt du?

D. Auf Wiedersehen, Karsten!

E. Gute Nacht!

F. Tag, Sonja!

D Complete the following dialogues.

Beispiel: TIM: Guten Tag, Herr Fischer!
HERR FISCHER: Guten Tag, Tim !

1. NELE: Tag, ______________ !
   FLORIAN: Tag, Nele.

2. Wie heißt du?
   ______________ heiße Sabine.

3. Angenehm, Michael!
   Es freut ______________ , Andreas.

4. Sprichst du arabisch, Günther?
   ______________ , ich spreche nicht arabisch.

5. Sprichst du japanisch, Masako?
   ______________ , ich spreche japanisch.

6. Sprichst du russisch, Boris?
   Ja, ich spreche ______________ .

7. Wie geht's, Benjamin?
   Gut, ______________ . Und dir?

8. Auf Wiedersehen, Stefan!
   ______________ morgen, Georg!

9. Danke, Frau Weber.
   ______________ , Johanna.

10. Wie heißt der Junge?
    Er ______________ Lukas Schneider.

Name: ______________________ Datum: ______________

E **Look closely at the German names of different countries. Since most of these words look similar to their English counterparts, you should have little difficulty understanding them. Under the appropriate headings, write the English name of the country and the German name of the language spoken there.**

das Land (country)	**Name auf Englisch** (English name)	**Sprache** (German name of language)
1. Deutschland	______________	______________
2. Italien	______________	______________
3. China	______________	______________
4. Russland	______________	______________
5. Spanien	______________	______________
6. England	______________	______________
7. Frankreich	______________	______________
8. Japan	______________	______________
9. Ägypten	______________	______________

F **Give German names to the girl and the boy in the following conversation. Write these names in the appropriate spaces and complete the dialogue.**

(Boy's name) ______________ : Tag! Wie heißt ______________ ?

(Girl's name) ______________ : Ich heiße ______________ . Und du?

(Boy's name) ______________ : Ich ______________ .

(Girl's name) ______________ : Es ______________ mich.

(Boy's name) ______________ : ______________ .

Name: ______________________________ Datum: ______________________

G ***Zum Sprechen.* Imagine that it's the first day of school. You and your partner play the roles of two students who haven't met yet. Carry on a short conversation in German in which each of you tries to find out as much information as you can about the other. Limit your questions to those you have already practiced in class and be sure to respond appropriately to your partner's questions or comments. For example, you might:**

1. say *hello* or *hi* to your partner
2. ask your partner what his/her name is
3. ask your partner how he/she is
4. tell you partner *good luck*
5. tell your partner *good-bye* and *see you later*

H **Word Search *(Buchstabensalat)*. Find and circle the German equivalent for each of the nine English words, names, or expressions listed. Although some expressions contain two words each, they will appear as one in this puzzle. Words may go forward, backward, up, down, or diagonally.**

S E N E F P P N E G R O M S I B R
T H N V K B I C I X L Y X D T F V
G Z Y T F N B J Z A T O N K K W I
H L A B S T N U B P R E Q I P F M
I V I A Z C N T H B B Q M J O T L
S X X S A P H E R A T N Z A L I V
G G U B M K I U N X E L S Z J V J
U X Z W Z R Q E L M E H B R J J M
T Q S K A E T Y A D O N V L V W X
E U G M Z U F N S K I B I W M N X
N H D W G N H Y I M C G A K Q E F
T Q I H P I E V N E F P U F L U I
A M Y S L V A R C W S Q Q N P A H
G A O X I L D D A F C K K G G Q S
T I M A L L P T Z B I T T E Q N S

1. excuse me
2. Marie
3. good evening
4. names
5. please
6. Niklas
7. hello
8. see you tomorrow
9. yes

Name: ______________________ Datum: ______________

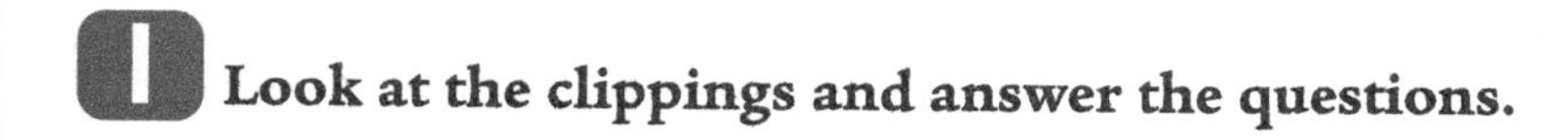

Look at the clippings and answer the questions.

Meine Adresse: 2006 6019 1079910

❑ Frau ❑ Herr (Bitte in Blockschrift ausfüllen!)

Name

Vorname

Straße, Nr.

PLZ Ort

Telefon (für evtl. Rückfragen) Geburtsdatum

Borek-Kunden-Nr. (falls bekannt) E-Mail

1. An order form requires you to fill out your name and address. What polite word tells you to fill out this form in block letters?

   ____

2. This form has places for the two parts of your name. What part of your name goes above the word *Name*?

   ____

3. What part of your name is to be written above the word *Vorname*?

   ____

4. Is this order form intended for a child or an adult?

   ____

5. What do you think the initials *PLZ* before *Ort* (town) stand for in English?

   ____

6. What is the German equivalent of "A very warm welcome!"?

____

7. When is the mug supposed to be used?

____

8. An insect called a *Marienkäfer* is a symbol of something we all want. What?

____

9. What does the word *Danke* express?

____

10. Can you guess what the word *Welt* means in the *Hallo Welt* headline? (Hint: Look at the globe.)

____

Name: ______________________ Datum: ______________________

UNIT 2

A How is each object used? Match each object with its description.

_____	1. ein Buch	A. lets in fresh air and daylight
_____	2. ein Fenster	B. place to put waste paper
_____	3. ein Bild	C. makes a plain room look more attractive
_____	4. ein Papierkorb	D. opens up new worlds of adventure and information
_____	5. eine Landkarte	E. shows you geographical locations

B Identify each of the following illustrations. *(Auf Deutsch, bitte.)*

1. 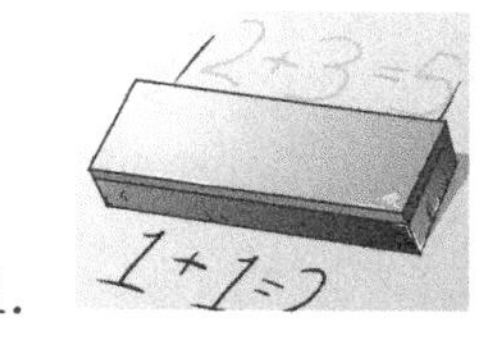 Das ist ein ______________________ .

2. 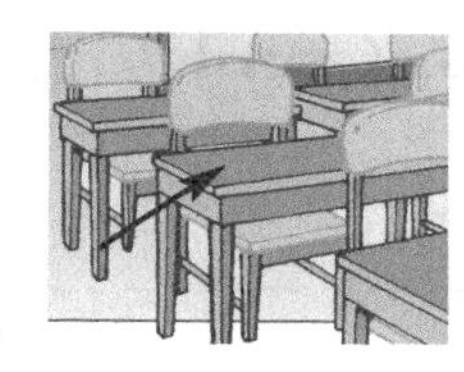 Das ist ein ______________________ .

3. 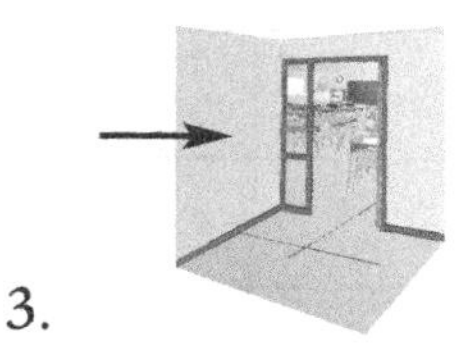 Das ist eine ______________________ .

4. 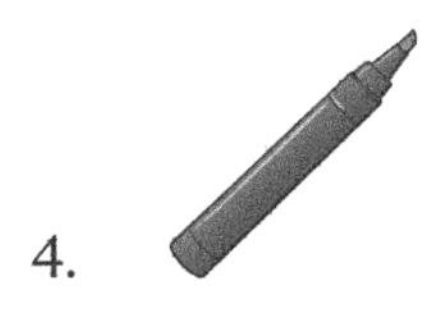 Das ist ein ______________________ .

5.  Das ist ein ______________________ .

Name: ______________________ Datum: ______________________

6. Das ist ein ______________________.

7. Das ist ein ______________________.

8. Das ist ein ______________________.

9. Das ist ein ______________________.

10. Das ist eine ______________________.

C Name the classroom object most closely associated with each group of words. *(Auf Deutsch, bitte.)* Include the article *(ein, eine)* for each word.

1. alarm, digital ______________________
2. Uruguay, Norway ______________________
3. *The Adventures of Tom Sawyer, Harry Potter* ______________________
4. loose-leaf, graph ______________________
5. straight back, armless ______________________

D List five items you might carry in your school backpack!

1. ______________________
2. ______________________
3. ______________________
4. ______________________
5. ______________________

Name: ______________________________ Datum: ______________________

E Find your way through the *Klassenzimmer*. Name the classroom objects you encounter on your way.

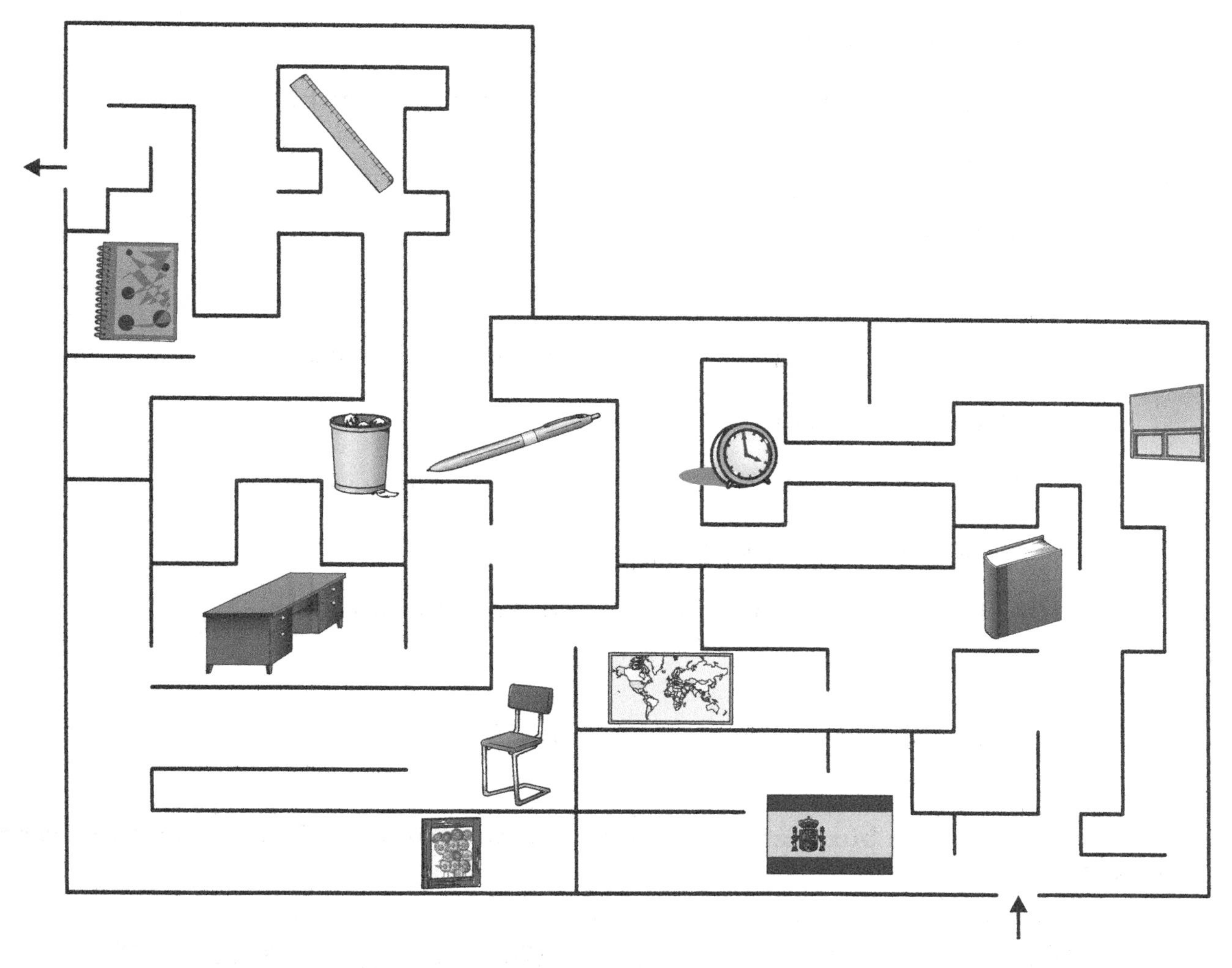

1. ______________________________

2. ______________________________

3. ______________________________

4. ______________________________

5. ______________________________

Name: ______________________________ Datum: ______________________

F **Your friend tells you in German to do certain things. What does each command mean? Choose either A or B.**

_____ 1. Schreib auf Deutsch!

A. Write in German. B. Say it in German.

_____ 2. Lies!

A. Speak. B. Read.

_____ 3. Heb die Hand!

A. Raise your hand. B. Go to the board.

_____ 4. Mach das Buch zu!

A. Open the book. B. Close the book.

_____ 5. Nimm ein Blatt Papier heraus!

A. Take out a sheet of paper. B. Turn on the computer.

_____ 6. Sprich!

A. Speak. B. Listen.

G **Find the word in the box that best completes each command. Then write it in the space provided.**

deutsch	Tafel	Buch	Computer	Hand	Frage	Bild

1. Heb die ______________________________!
2. Sprich ______________________________!
3. Geh an die ______________________________!
4. Beantworte die ______________________________!
5. Schalte den ______________________________ an!
6. Zeichne ein ______________________________!
7. Mach das ______________________________ auf!

Name: ______________________ Datum: ______________

H **Write a command suggested by each item.**

1. ein Bleistift: ______________________
2. ein Buch: ______________________
3. die Musik: ______________________
4. das Fenster: ______________________
5. den Computer: ______________________

I ***Zum Sprechen.* As you point to various classroom objects, ask a classmate for the German name of each one, including the words *ein* or *eine*. Give her/him a set time, for example, two minutes. Keep a record of how many mistakes are made. Then reverse the roles. You also get the same set time (two minutes). The winner is the person with fewer errors recorded before the time expires.**

J **Working in pairs, take turns giving commands to each other. Use all the commands presented in Unit 2.**

K **Look at the clippings and then answer the questions.**

Lineal
dcm & cm-Teilung
D5-88703 6,90 €

Deutsch

Druckschrift
a b c d e f g h i
j k l m n o p qu
r s t u v w x y z
ä ö ü ß
ABCDEFGHI
JKLMNOPQu
RSTUVWXYZ
ÄÖÜ

Schrifttafel - Druckschrift
120016 € 49,00 € 53,36

1. Translate the word above the alphabet chart.

   ____

2. What word indicates printing or writing with block letters?

   ____

3. What letters are included in the German alphabet but not in the English alphabet?

   ____

4. Where in the alphabet do these special letters appear?

   ____

Name: ______________________ Datum: ______________________

5. Which special letter appears only in lowercase?

____

6. This classroom alphabet chart is offered for sale. What is the price?

____

7. How many centimeters long is the *Lineal*?

____

8. What is the price of the *Lineal*?

____

Name: ______________________ Datum: ______________________

UNIT 3

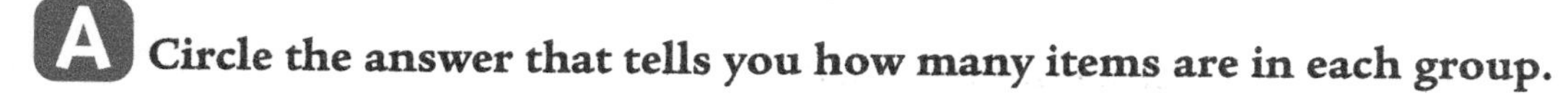

A Circle the answer that tells you how many items are in each group.

1. A. sechzehn B. elf C. neun

2. A. fünfzehn B. vierzehn C. drei

3. A. acht B. sechs C. zwölf

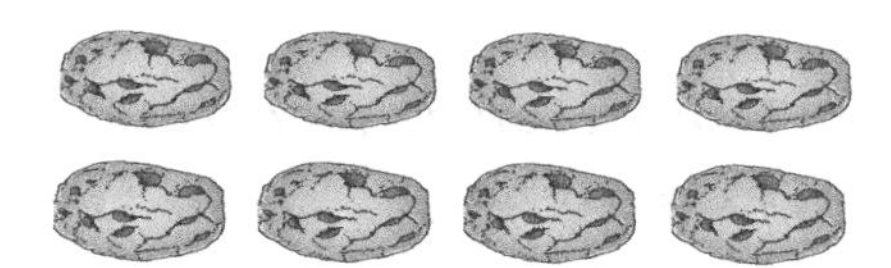

4. A. sieben B. elf C. vier

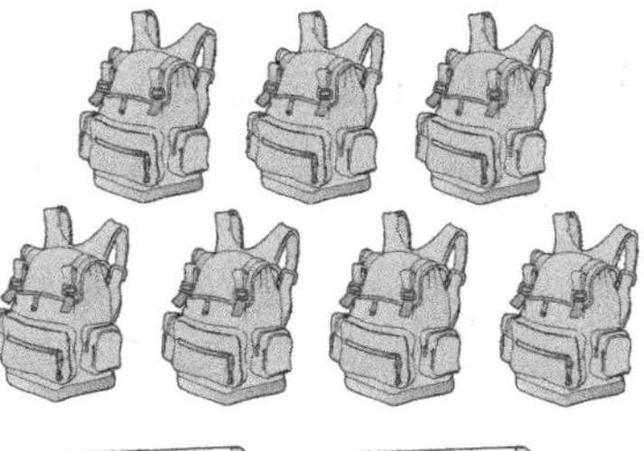

5. A. dreizehn B. zehn C. zwei

6. A. acht B. vier C. zwanzig

Name: ______________________________ Datum: ______________________

B Match the Arabic numerals with the words.

_____	1. 2	A. dreizehn
_____	2. 8	B. achtunddreißig
_____	3. 13	C. zweiundneunzig
_____	4. 5	D. fünf
_____	5. 21	E. einundzwanzig
_____	6. 38	F. siebenundsiebzig
_____	7. 77	G. zwei
_____	8. 11	H. elf
_____	9. 59	I. neunundfünfzig
_____	10. 92	J. acht

C Numerical sequences. Find the common pattern and then write the missing number in German.

1. achtzehn, ______________________________, zwanzig
2. zwei, ______________________________, sechs
3. fünf, ______________________________, fünfzehn
4. vierzig, ______________________________, sechzig
5. siebzig, ______________________________, neunzig

D Wie viele? Beantworte die Fragen auf Deutsch. *(Answer the questions in German.)*

1. How many planets are there in our solar system? ______________
2. How many toes does a person have? ______________
3. How many legs does a horse have? ______________
4. How many weeks make up a year? ______________
5. How many letters are there in the English alphabet? ______________
6. How many items make a dozen? ______________
7. How many minutes are there in a half-hour? ______________
8. How many seconds are there in a minute? ______________
9. How many days are there in January? ______________
10. How many hearts do you have? ______________

E Express each sentence as an equation.

Beispiel: Zehn geteilt durch zwei ist fünf.
$10 \div 2 = 5$

1. Dreißig weniger zwanzig ist zehn. ______________
2. Zweihundert und zweihundert ist vierhundert. ______________
3. Dreizehn mal eins ist dreizehn. ______________
4. Zwanzig geteilt durch vier ist fünf. ______________

Name: ______________________ Datum: ______________________

Solve the following arithmetic problems in German. Answer each question by writing a complete sentence in German.

> **Beispiel:** Wie viel ist neunzig weniger achtzig?
> Neunzig weniger achtzig ist zehn.

1. Wie viel ist drei mal vier?

____

2. Wie viel ist sieben und fünfzehn?

____

3. Wie viel ist tausend weniger zweihundert?

____

4. Wie viel sechzehn geteilt durch acht?

____

5. Wie viel ist dreißig und vierzig?

____

6. Wie viel ist neun weniger fünf?

____

7. Wie viel ist siebenundzwanzig geteilt durch drei?

____

8. Wie viel ist vierzehn mal eins?

____

9. Wie viel ist zwölf und eins?

____

10. Wie viel ist fünfundsechzig weniger vier?

____

Name: ______________________ Datum: ______________________

G **How many things are there in your classroom? Answer each question by writing a complete sentence in German.**

> **Beispiel:** Wie viele Lineale *(rulers)* gibt es?
> Es gibt neunundzwanzig Lineale.

1. Wie viele Hefte *(notebooks)* gibt es?

____

2. Wie viele Bücher *(books)* gibt es?

____

3. Wie viele Fahnen *(flags)* gibt es?

____

4. Wie viele Fenster *(windows)* gibt es?

____

H **How much does something cost? Answer each question by writing a complete sentence in German.**

> **Beispiel:** Wie viel kostet ein Buch?
> Ein Buch kostet zehn Euro (€).

1. Wie viel kostet ein Bleistift?

____

2. Wie viel kostet ein Computer?

____

3. Wie viel kostet ein Kuli?

____

4. Wie viel kostet ein Lineal?

____

5. Wie viel kostet eine Fahne?

____

Name: ______________________________ Datum: ______________________

I ***Zum Sprechen.*** **With a partner see how good you are with numbers. Each of you receives 25 points at the beginning. Whenever either of you makes a mistake counting, subtract one point. To begin, start counting from zero and then suddenly stop. Your partner must continue counting and then stop at any time. You should be quick enough to pick up where your partner stopped. Continue counting and alternating until you reach 50 or another previously designated number. The player with more points at the end wins.**

J **The European Central Bank distributes a brochure that explains the Euro currency. On this page you see both bills and coins.** ***(Beantworte die Fragen auf Deutsch, bitte.)***

DIE ACHT EURO-MÜNZEN

DEUTSCHLAND

Die 1- und 2-Euro-Münzen zeigen den Bundesadler, das traditionelle Symbol deutscher Souveränität.
Das Brandenburger Tor als Symbol für die Teilung und spätere Wiedervereinigung Deutschlands erscheint auf den 10-, 20- und 50-Cent-Münzen.
Der Eichenzweig auf den 1-, 2- und 5-Cent-Münzen erinnert an das Motiv der deutschen Pfennigmünzen.

1. A *Geldschein* (or just *Schein* for short) is a bill. How many different denominations of *Scheine* are there? ____________________
2. What is the value of the most expensive *Schein?* ____________________
3. How many *Münzen* are there? ____________________
4. On how many *Münzen* do you see the oak leaf symbol? ____________________
5. What value does the least expensive *Euro* coin have? ____________________
6. How much money do you have when you add the amount of the three coins that show the *Brandenburger Tor?* ____________________

Name: ______________________ Datum: ______________

Unit 4

A What is special about each city? Match the city with the description.

_____ 1. Leipzig A. site of a Gothic cathedral

_____ 2. Dresden B. site of fine porcelain and paintings

_____ 3. Berlin C. site of the *Gewandhaus* Orchestra

_____ 4. München D. site of the Brandenburg Gate

_____ 5. Köln E. site of the *Oktoberfest*

B Select the letter of each correct answer.

_____ 1. Which river flows through Dresden and Hamburg?

A. die Donau B. der Rhein C. die Elbe

_____ 2. Where is the North Sea?

A. northwest of Germany B. south of Germany C. northeast of Germany

_____ 3. Which city is also Germany's largest seaport?

A. München B. Leipzig C. Hamburg

_____ 4. Where are the Alps?

A. in the center B. in the south C. in the north

_____ 5. Where is Austria located?

A. north of Poland B. east of Switzerland C. west of Germany

Name: ______________________ Datum: ______________________

C **Look at the map of Switzerland, Austria, and Germany. You will see 16 numbers, each of which indicates a city or a river. (For rivers, the dot for each number is placed directly on the white line indicating the river.) Identify each number in the space provided on the next page. Choose from:**

Rivers	**Cities in Switzerland**	**Cities in Austria**	**Cities in Germany**	
die Donau	Bern	Salzburg	Berlin	Hamburg
die Elbe	Genf	Wien	Dresden	Köln
der Rhein	Zürich		Leipzig	München
der Main			Frankfurt am Main	

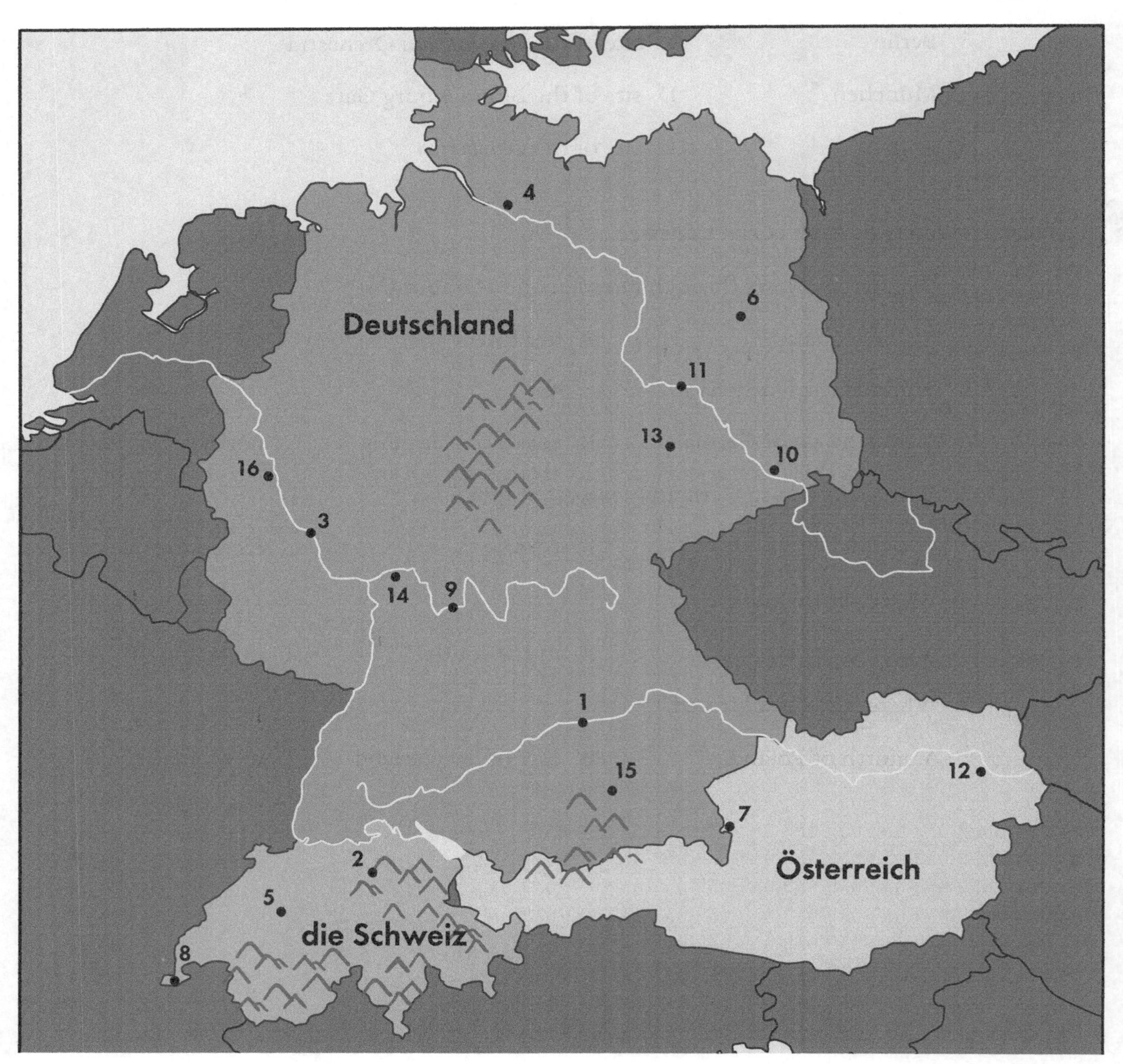

Name: ______________________ Datum: ______________

Each number below corresponds to the same number on the map. Write each name.

1. ______________________ 9. ______________________
2. ______________________ 10. ______________________
3. ______________________ 11. ______________________
4. ______________________ 12. ______________________
5. ______________________ 13. ______________________
6. ______________________ 14. ______________________
7. ______________________ 15. ______________________
8. ______________________ 16. ______________________

D ***Zum Sprechen.*** **Imagine that you are inquiring at a travel agency about a trip to the German-speaking area of Europe. Ask your partner, a travel agent, about what you should see and do there. Ask what you should pack for a two-week stay. Decide on a particular month so you can plan appropriate clothing. Then reverse roles, so that your partner asks you questions and you answer.**

E **Identify each place by name and its location.**

1. Bodensee: ______________________
2. Nordssee: ______________________
3. Ostsee: ______________________
4. Alpen: ______________________
5. Harz: ______________________

Name: ______________________ Datum: ______________

F **Look at the maps of Switzerland, Austria, and Germany in your textbook. Identify the direction you travel from one city to another. Use the following codes: N (north), S (south), E (east), W (west), NE (northeast), NW (northwest), SE (southeast), and SW (southwest).**

FROM	TO	DIRECTION
1. München	Hamburg	________
2. Berlin	Dresden	________
3. Wien	Salzburg	________
4. Salzburg	Köln	________
5. Bern	Leipzig	________
6. Zürich	Genf	________
7. Frankfurt	Wien	________
8. München	Wien	________

G **Flüsse *(Rivers)*. Beantworte die Fragen!**

1. Which river flows from east to west? ______________________
2. Which river flows from south to northwest? ______________________
3. Which river flows through Hamburg? ______________________
4. Which river is called the Danube? ______________________
5. On which river is the city of Köln located? ______________________

Name: ______________________ Datum: ______________________

H Kreuzworträtsel

Waagerecht

3. small country between Switzerland and Austria
5. Germany
7. city located on a lake in southwest of Switzerland
8. "Venice of the North"
11. city known for trade fairs
12. site of the Bradenburg Gate
13. body of water northeast of Germany

Senkrecht

1. river in central Germany
2. originally a Roman colony
4. hometown of W.A. Mozart
5. river that flows through Vienna
6. body of water northwest of Germany
9. "Florence of the North"
10. capital of Österreich

Name: ______________________ Datum: ______________________

I **Look at the clippings and then answer the questions.**

1. What country is inviting you to visit?

____

2. For what kind of vacation is this country well known?

____

3. What season is recommended for this type of vacation?

____

4. What kind of information is contained in the catalog?

____

5. Would this catalog interest someone who likes *Natur*?

____

6. Name another way one can really see this country.

____

7. A southern region in this country starts with the letter K. What is its name?

____

8. Find the German word for "mountains."

____

Name: ______________________ Datum: ______________________

UNIT 5

A Where does one usually do the following things? Match the activity with the place.

_____	1. cook	A. Garten
_____	2. sleep	B. Wohnzimmer
_____	3. take a shower	C. Küche
_____	4. eat	D. Schlafzimmer
_____	5. park the car	E. Badezimmer
_____	6. plant flowers	F. Esszimmer
_____	7. receive visitors	G. Garage

B What could you find in each room? Circle the appropriate item.

1. *das Wohnzimmer:*

dishwasher   recliner   bathtub   spare tires

2. *das Badezimmer:*

computer   blender   forks   shower

3. *die Küche:*

refrigerator   bed   desk   toilet

4. *das Schlafzimmer:*

lawn mower   kitchen table   bedspread   washing machine

5. *die Garage:*

plates   automotive tools   pillowcases   bookcase

6. *das Esszimmer:*

broom   clothes closet   snow shovel   tablecloth

Name: ______________________ Datum: ______________

C **Below are four answers to some missing questions. For each answer write a question about the words in boldface.**

1. Frage *(Question):* ______________________?

   Antwort *(Answer):* Ich wohne **in einem Haus.**

2. Frage: ______________________?

   Antwort: Es gibt **drei** Schlafzimmer.

3. Frage: ______________________?

   Antwort: Die Küche ist **hinter dem Esszimmer.**

4. Frage: ______________________?

   Antwort: Es gibt **ein** Badezimmer.

D ***Ergänze den Dialog!*** **Pretend that you are Stefan and complete your answers during an interview with Sabine.**

1. SABINE: Wo ist dein Haus?

   STEFAN: Mein Haus ist in ______________. *(city)*

2. SABINE: Ist die Garage hinter dem Haus?

   STEFAN: ______________, die Garage ist hinter dem Haus.

3. SABINE: Wie viele Schlafzimmer gibt es in deinem *(your)* Haus?

   STEFAN: Es gibt ______________ Schlafzimmer in meinem *(my)* Haus.

4. SABINE: Gibt es ein Wohnzimmer?

   STEFAN: ______________, na klar!

5. SABINE: Wie viele Badezimmer gibt es?

   STEFAN: Es ______________ ein Badezimmer.

6. SABINE: Gibt es Blumen *(flowers)* in dem Garten?

   STEFAN: Ja, es gibt ______________.

Name: ______________________ Datum: ______________________

E **Find your way back to your bed. Name each type of house or shelter you encounter on your way.**

1. ______________________
2. ______________________
3. ______________________
4. ______________________
5. ______________________

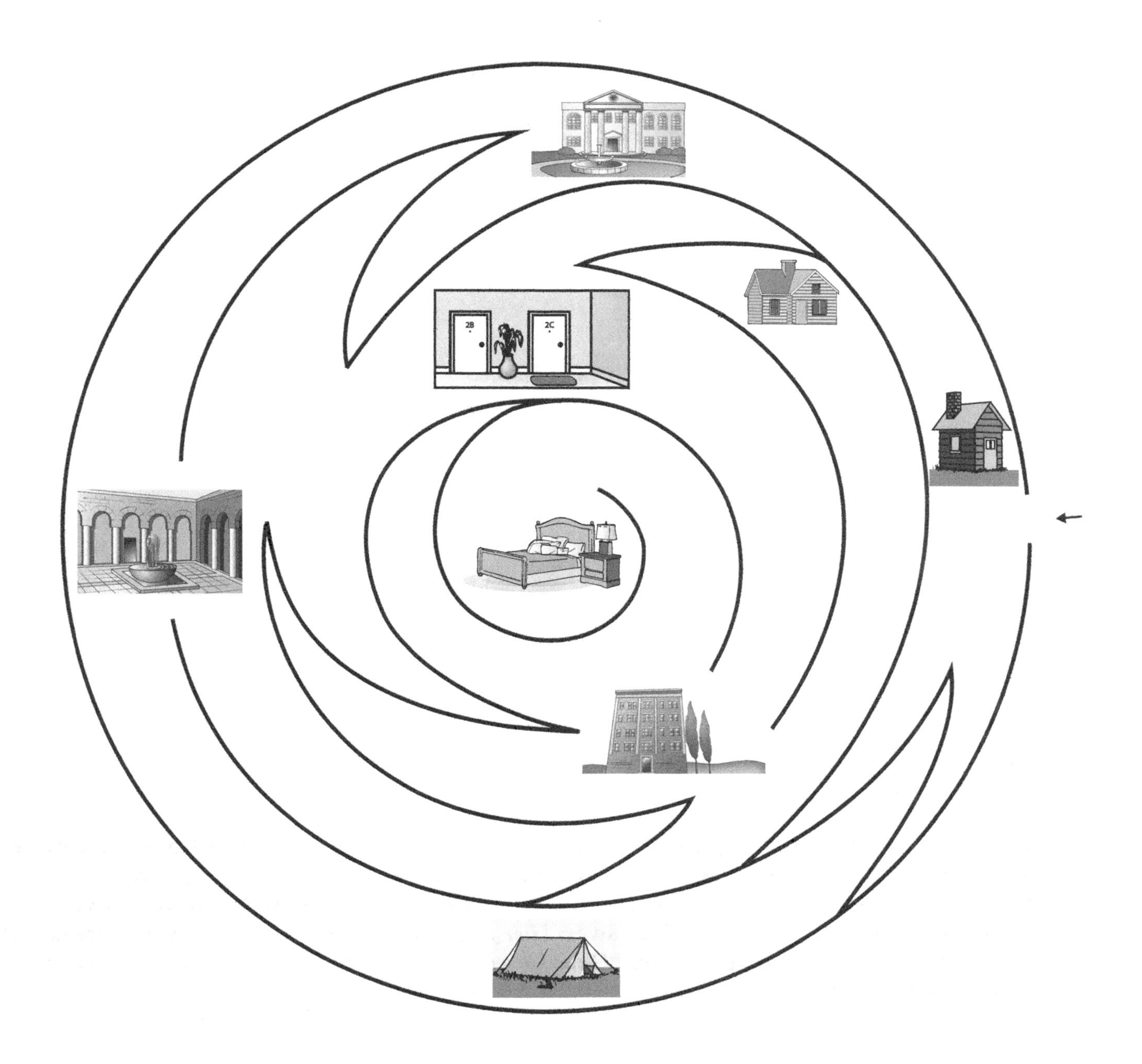

Name: ______________________________ Datum: ____________________

F **Be an architect! Draw a floor plan of your dream house, showing where all the rooms are. Label the rooms in German.**

G ***Zum Sprechen.* Working in pairs, give your partner a tour of the dream house you drew above. Point out different rooms and other features, saying *Hier ist . . .* (Here is . . .). Your partner will then ask you the location of several rooms that you have not yet mentioned *(Wo ist . . . ?)*. You will answer: *Hier ist . . .* or *Da drüben ist . . .* (Over there is . . .). When the tour is finished, say *Dein Haus ist sehr schön. Danke.* Then reverse the roles, using your friend's dream house.**

Name: ______________________ Datum: ______________________

Wo wohnt . . . ? Beantworte jede Frage mit dem Namen einer Stadt! ***(Answer each question completely with the name of a city.)***

Beispiel: Wo wohnt Erich? (eine Stadt in der Schweiz)
Erich wohnt in Bern.

1. Wo wohnt Frau Schmidt? (eine Stadt in Österrreich)

____

2. Wo wohnt Herr Weber? (eine Stadt in der Schweiz)

____

3. Wo wohnt Elisabeth? (eine Stadt in Deutschland)

____

4. Wo wohnt die Familie Meier? (eine Stadt in Deutschland)

____

5. Wo wohnt Klaus? (eine Stadt in Österrreich)

____

I **Look at the clippings and then answer the questions.**

... für ein gemütliches Zuhause

Frische Ideen ...

Wohnen Sie sich glücklich!

1. A nicely decorated house can make you *glücklich!* What do you think this word means?

   ____

2. The two magazines can give you *frische Ideen* to help you create a cozy home. What are *frische Ideen?*

   ____

3. What does *Kreativ Magazin* feature on its cover? *(Auf Englisch, bitte.)*

   ____

4. *Wie viel kostet das Magazin Lisa?*

   ____

5. Name the room pictured on the cover of *Lisa. (Auf Deutsch, bitte.)*

   ____

6. Identify the English equivalents of these words: *dekorieren, Haus, Atmospäre, Magazin:*

   ____

Name: ______________________ Datum: ______________

UNIT 6

A Match the English with the German.

_____	1. godparents	A.	Junge
_____	2. girl	B.	Enkel
_____	3. child	C.	Onkel
_____	4. boy	D.	Kind
_____	5. niece	E.	Kusine
_____	6. aunt	F.	Neffe
_____	7. grandson	G.	Tante
_____	8. nephew	H.	Nichte
_____	9. cousin	I.	Mädchen
_____	10. uncle	J.	Paten

B Ergänze die Sätze. *(Complete the sentences with the names of family members.)*

_____ 1. Der Sohn von meinem Bruder ist mein . . .

A. Neffe B. Onkel C. Cousin

_____ 2. Die Schwester von meiner Mutter ist meine . . .

A. Patin B. Großmutter C. Tante

_____ 3. Die Kinder von meinen Eltern sind meine . . .

A. Brüder und Schwestern B. Cousins und Kusinen C. Onkel und Tanten

_____ 4. Mein Bruder ist der . . . von meinen Großeltern.

A. Neffe B. Enkel C. Sohn

_____ 5. Die Tochter von meinem Onkel ist meine . . .

A. Kusine B. Tante C. Großmutter

Name: ______________________________ Datum: ______________________

_____ 6. Meine Mutter ist die . . . von meinem Vater.

A. Tante B. Schwester C. Frau

_____ 7. Mein Vater und meine Mutter sind meine . . .

A. Großeltern B. Paten C. Eltern

_____ 8. Meine Großeltern und meine Tanten und Onkel sind meine . . .

A. Schwestern B. Verwandten C. Eltern

C *Zeichne ein Bild!* (Draw a picture using a separate sheet of paper. Stick figures will be fine!)

1. Draw yourself. Label: *Das bin ich!*
2. Identify yourself by name: *Ich heiße . . .*
3. Draw a cousin, sister, or brother:
4. Label and name as follows: If you choose a boy, write: *Das ist mein . . . (Cousin, Bruder). Er heißt . . .* (Write in his name.) If you choose a girl, write: *Das ist meine Kusine/Schwester). Sie heißt . . .* (Write in her name.)

D In the spaces below, write in the names of your favorite television or storybook family. Use only the family members below that apply to your particular selection.

Name of TV show or book ______________________________

1. die Mutter ______________________________
2. der Vater ______________________________
3. der Bruder ______________________________
4. die Schwester ______________________________
5. der Onkel ______________________________
6. die Tante ______________________________
7. die Großmutter ______________________________
8. der Großvater ______________________________

Name: ______________________ Datum: ______________

E **Wie viele?** ***(Answer questions about how many relatives you have.)***

Beispiele: Wie viele Cousins hast du? *(. . . do you have)?*
Ich habe keine *(I don't have any)* Cousins./Ich habe einen *(I have one)* Cousin.
Wie viele Kusinen hast du?
Ich habe keine Kusinen./Ich habe eine Kusine.

1. Wie viele Brüder hast du?

____

2. Wie viele Schwestern hast du?

____

3. Wie viele Cousins hast du?

____

4. Wie viele Kusinen hast du?

____

5. Wie viele Onkel hast du?

____

6. Wie viele Tanten hast du?

____

7. Wie viele Neffen hast du?

____

8. Wie viele Nichten hast du?

____

Name: ______________________ Datum: ______________________

F **Make a list of your family and relatives. State their relationship to you *(auf Deutsch)* and their ages.**

____

____

____

____

____

____

____

____

____

____

G **Beantworte die Fragen auf Deutsch! *(Short answers)***

1. Wie heißt du? ______________________
2. Hast du eine Schwester? ______________________
3. Wie viele Cousins hast du? ______________________
4. Wie heißt dein Vater? ______________________
5. Hast du einen Stiefbruder? ______________________

Name: ____________________ Datum: ____________________

H Kreuzworträtsel

ß = SS

Waagerecht

1. child
3. niece
5. stepfather
10. grandson
11. aunt
12. mother
13. girl

Senkrecht

1. cousin (female)
2. stepsister
4. grandfather
6. parents
7. boy
8. godfather
9. wife

Name: ______________________________ Datum: ______________________

Look at the stamps and ad and then answer the questions.

Stamps

1. What do all the stamps have in common?

____

2. *Wie viele Briefmarken gibt es?*

____

3. One stamp shows the number 55. What does that signify?

____

4. What do you think the message on the *10 Cent* stamp is?

____

Vacation Ad

5. What phrase or sentence suggests that families will like these places?

____

6. How many sites are listed for the *Nordsee* region? *(Auf Deutsch, bitte.)*

____

7. What contact information is provided in this list?

____

8. Besides *Deutschland,* what other country is listed in this chart?

____

Anzeige

Hier machen Familien gern Urlaub

◆NORDSEE
Föhr Touristik e.V.
Tel. 04681-300, Fax -30 50
Spiekeroog
Tel. 01805-88 75 88, Fax 04976-91 93 47
◆OSTSEE/SCHLESWIG-HOLSTEIN
Heiligenhafen Tourist GmbH
Tel. 04362-907 20, Fax -39 38
Hohwachter Bucht Touristik
Tel. 04381-905 50, Fax -90 55 55
IFA Ferienzentrum Südstrand
Tel. 04371-890, Fax -89 20 00
Kurverwaltung Schwedeneck
Tel. 04308-331, Fax -12 60
Tourismus-Service Fehmarn
Tel. 04371-866 86 86, Fax -50 63 16
Wongel Ostseeappartements
Tel. 04503-741 89, Fax -748 43
Wulfener Hals, Fehmarn
Tel. 04371-862 80, Fax -37 23
◆SCHLESWIG-HOLSTEIN
Herzogtum Lauenburg
Tel. 04541-80 21 10, Fax -80 21 12
◆RÜGEN
Aquamaris Strandresidenz Rügen
Tel. 038391-444 05, Fax -441 41
◆MECKLENBURGISCHE SEENPLATTE
Dorfhotel Fleesensee
Tel. 039932-803 00, Fax -80 30 20
Müritzparadies
Tel. 039823-2530, Fax -25 32 32
◆NORDRHEIN-WESTFALEN
Kur & Freizeit GmbH Schmallenberger Sauerland
Tel. 02972-974 00, Fax -97 40 26
◆NIEDERSACHSEN
Bädergesellschaft Bad Sachsa mbH
Tel. 05523-95 09 60, Fax -94 50 80
Sarcon Ferienpark Grafschaft Bentheim
Tel. 0800-8634300 gebührenfrei
Südsee-Camp
Tel. 05196-98 01 11, Fax -98 02 99
◆BADEN-WÜRTTEMBERG
Tourist-Information Baiersbronn
Tel. 07442-84 14 41, Fax -84 14 48
Tourist-Information Schluchsee
Tel. 07656-77 32, Fax -77 59
◆OBERBAYERN
Ruhpolding Tourismus GmbH
Tel. 08663-88 60, Fax -880 20
Tourismusverband Pfaffenwinkel
Tel. 08861-77 73, Fax -20 06 78
◆OSTBAYERN
Tourist Information Bodenmais
Tel. 09924-77 81 30, Fax -77 81 46
◆ALLGÄU
Alpsee-Grünten
Tel. 08321-61 52 91, Fax -61 52 93
Bad Hindelang
Tel. 08324-89 20, Fax -80 55
Tourist Information Schwangau
Tel. 08362-81 98-0, Fax -81 98 25
◆ÖSTERREICH
Tourismusverband Paznaun Silvrettaregion
Tel. +43 (0) 5445-62 43 11, Fax -61 63
Berghotel Hochfügen, Zillertal
Tel. +43 (0) 5280-53 12, Fax -53 12 50
Hotel Filzmooserhof, Salzburger Land
Tel. +43 (0) 6453-82 32, Fax -82 32 66
VillachWarmbad * Faaker See * Ossiacher See
Tel. +43 (0) 4242-42 00 00, Fax -420 00 42
◆SÜDTIROL
Südtirol's Süden
Tel. +39-0471-63 34 88, Fax -63 33 67

Name: ______________________ Datum: ______________

UNIT 7

Zeichne die Tiere! **As best you can, draw the animals listed below. Then label each one with the words:** ***Das ist ein . . .*** **for a** ***der*** **or** ***das*** **word, and** ***Das ist eine . . .*** **for a** ***die*** **word.**

1. die Kuh:

3. der Vogel:

2. die Katze:

4. das Pferd:

B **Ich füttre . . .** ***(Which animal am I feeding? Use the clues to guess the correct animal. Write your answer in the space provided.)***

1. Oats; Arabian, Belgian, or Clydesdale

   Ich füttre das ______________________.

2. Corn; one of *The Three Little . . .*

   Ich füttre das ______________________.

3. Persian, Siamese, or Manx

   Ich füttre die ______________________.

4. Carrots; *Thumper* or *Bugs*

   Ich füttre das ______________________.

5. German pointer, Irish setter, or Newfoundland

   Ich füttre den ______________________.

6. Blue jay, cardinal, or robin

   Ich füttre den ______________________.

Name: ______________________ Datum: ______________________

C **Rearrange these animals from biggest to smallest:** ***das Schwein, das Pferd, die Ente, der Hund.***

____

____

____

____

D **Ergänze die Sätze auf Deutsch!**

1. Jutta und Simon sind auf dem *(country)* ______________________.
2. Es gibt viele ______________________.
3. Das Mädchen hat einen Apfel für das ______________________.
4. Der Junge kann ______________________.
5. Das Pferd heißt ______________________.

E **Wo sind diese Tiere? (*Where are these animals?*) *Complete the sentences by choosing the correct words from the word box.* Note: *die Kühe* (cows), *die Schweine* (pigs), *die Enten* (ducks), *die Vögel* (birds).**

Teich	Luft	Stall	Weide	Scheune

1. Die Kühe sind auf der ______________________.
2. Die Schweine sind im ______________________.
3. Die Hennen sind hinter der ______________________.
4. Die Enten sind auf dem ______________________.
5. Die Vögel sind in der ______________________.

Name: ______________________________ Datum: ____________________

F **Wie ist ein Tier?** ***(What are the animals like?) Describe the animals according to size: large* (groß) *or small* (klein).**

> **Beispiele:** Wie ist der Hund *(Saint Bernard)*?
> **You write:** Der Hund ist groß.
> Wie sind die Enten?
> **You write:** Die Enten sind klein.

1. Wie ist der Hund *(Chihuahua)*? ______________________________.
2. Wie ist die Katze? ______________________________.
3. Wie ist das Pferd? ______________________________.
4. Wie sind die Esel? ______________________________.
5. Wie sind die Hennen? ______________________________.

G **Can you guess the English meaning of each German sentence?**

_____ 1. Ich bin auf dem Lande.

A. I'm going to the country. B. I am in the country.

_____ 2. Ich sehe das Pferd.

A. I see the horse. B. I'm feeding the horse.

_____ 3. Ich möchte dir helfen.

A. I'd like to talk to you. B. I'd like to help you.

_____ 4. Du kannst den Eimer halten.

A. You can hold the pail. B. You can pet the rabbit.

_____ 5. Du kannst die Eier sammeln.

A. You can feed the goats. B. You can collect the eggs.

_____ 6. Ich füttre die Tiere.

A. I'm petting the animals. B. I'm feeding the animals.

_____ 7. Was machst du?

A. What are you doing? B. What do you have?

_____ 8. Ich streichle mein Kaninchen.

A. I'm petting my rabbit. B. I'm holding my pail.

Name: ______________________ Datum: ______________________

H ***Zum Sprechen.*** **Cut out pictures of the animals presented in this unit from magazines. Working with your partner, ask for the German word for each animal. Your partner will answer. Then change roles, and you answer this time.**

If you find pictures of animals you have not yet learned, look up their names in a German-English dictionary. You might want to label all your pictures and then hang them on a classroom wall. Label your display: *Die Tiere* (The Animals).

I **Word Search *(Buchstabensalat)*. Find and circle the German equivalent for each of the 15 English words listed. All the words appear in this unit. Remember that words may go forward, backward, up, down, or diagonally.**

X K J W N O G V V I P T F S S B O
A P G L I Q S V G B A B M O F F S
P A K T S R M D N A L X X N I J R
F D R E F P Y V O R H V M B L N A
E I C O X M C N J X J Y L Q E E C
L J Y T H Y J G Y B H K J X S Z T
P J O E Y V M K G D R U C E E P C
U N S N E H C N I N A K N P K K A
N H B U V F L O Q L D E Y D P W I
N C T H E J O V Y M U Z A M Q V F
R I J T X N D Z J O U T P K F L A
Q E L U N Z U G W X E A I Z L T V
A T J S I X W E I D E K G A B E O
T A B Y N Z Y W H B B K T F W Y G
I J K C S L U F T C T S K N P G E
X N T M A D I P P E S E V U R Q L
L G J T E E N T E Y I H K Y H T P

1. donkey
2. apple
3. cow
4. barn
5. horse
6. bird
7. stable
8. pond
9. rabbit
10. duck
11. pasture
12. country
13. cat
14. dog
15. air

Name: ______________________________ Datum: ______________

Look at the magazine cover first and then the classified ads to answer the questions.

Magazine Cover

1. What is the title of this magazine?

____

2. What does the title mean in English?

____

3. The cover's main title is *Wie uns Tiere helfen* or "How animals help ______________"

4. *Wie ist der Delphin* (dolphin)?

____

Name: ______________________ Datum: ______________

Classified Ads

5. How many dogs are looking for homes? *(Auf Deutsch, bitte.)*

____

6. What kind of kittens are for sale?

____

7. What is the German word for parakeets?

____

8. What other animals are for sale?

____

Sonthofen 

HUNDE

Husky sucht Pflegeplatz. Tel. 0831/570815

Hobbyzüchter verk. Westiwelp., m.Impf.+ St.b., 330 €. 09932/1298

Mischling–Welpe w ca. 11 Wo. aus Griechenland, weiß–beige, sehr lieb, geimpft su. liebev. zuhause. Tel. 0831/5204222

KATZEN

Perser– + Exot.Babies, 10 Wo., 3 m., bl.sm., bl.cr., w., v. Priv. Tel. 08231/917793

www.perserkatzen-allgaeu.de Perser– u. Exotic–Shorthair–Babies aus liebev. Hobby–Zucht zu verk. T. 08321/87542

VÖGEL

Haben noch junge Wellensittiche abzugeben. 10,–. 0151/11686959

PFERDE

12 j. Württ. Fuchsstute Weltmeyer–Linie, Stm 169, geeign. f. Freizeit + Turniereinstieg; kein Anfängerpferd, VB 2.800,–. 0172/6566503, 19 h

Hübsche, temperamentvolle, braune Spaniermix–Stute, STM 1,58, Western/Englisch u. mit Pferdeflüstererkenntnissen geritten ca. 13 J. alt, zus. mit Ponyfreundin ca. 9J., schw.–weiß gefleckt an guten Platz abzug. VB. Tel. 08373/987553

Name: ______________________ Datum: ______________________

UNIT 8

A Match the job titles with the job skills and descriptions.

_____ 1. Mechaniker

_____ 3. Koch

_____ 4. Elektrikerin

_____ 5. Tischler

_____ 5. Ärztin

_____ 6. Schauspieler

_____ 7. Musikerin

_____ 8. Klempner

_____ 9. Landwirtin

_____ 10. Künstler

A. can play an instrument

B. knows how and when to plant crops

C. can help you take care of your health

D. has a good sense of color and perspective

E. knows how to fix an engine

F. can create appetizing meals

G. imitates gestures and memorizes words easily

H. knows how to make wooden cabinets

I. knows how to install an electrical outlet

J. can repair a leaking faucet

B Circle the letter of the word most closely associated with each description.

1. der Arzt/die Ärztin

   A. anatomy B. music C. botany

2. der Musiker/die Musikerin

   A. geography B. fashion C. band

3. die Landwirtin/der Landwirt

   A. art B. agriculture C. literature

4. der Geschäftsmann/die Geschäftsfrau

   A. drama B. engineering C. marketing

5. der Koch/die Köchin

   A. nutrition B. history C. mathematics

6. die Schauspielerin/der Schauspieler

   A. health B. physics C. drama

C Name the person needed in each of the following circumstances. The letters *M* and *F* refer to a male or female person.

> **Beispiel:** Your parents' car will not start. You say, "I'm calling a . . . mechanic." *(M)*
> Ich rufe einen Mechaniker an.

1. You have injured your ankle. *(M)*

   Ich rufe einen ______________________________ an.

2. You need someone to paint your portrait as a surprise present for your parents. *(F)*

   Ich rufe eine ______________________________ an.

3. You and your family need someone to build new cabinets in the kitchen. *(M)*

   Ich rufe einen ______________________________ an.

4. You discover that the bathroom sink is clogged. *(F)*

   Ich rufe eine ______________________________ an.

5. You find that the lamp keeps flickering on and off. *(M)*

   Ich rufe einen ______________________________ an.

6. You need advice about how to make low-calorie meals. *(F)*

   Ich rufe eine ______________________________ an.

7. You are having trouble installing a new program on your computer. *(M)*

   Ich rufe einen ______________________________ an. *(M)*

8. You are making a movie and need a woman to play a character.

   Ich rufe eine ______________________________ an. *(F)*

9. You invented a new product and need someone to sell it for you. *(M)*

   Ich rufe einen ______________________________ an.

10. Your grandfather is ill. Your family needs to find someone to take care of him during the day. *(F)*

    Ich rufe eine ______________________________ an.

Name: ______________________ Datum: ______________________

D **Ergänze den Dialog.** *(Complete the dialogue by using the words in the box.)*

Briefträger	Köchin	ist	Programmiererin
arbeite	machst	Krankenpfleger	Arbeitsstelle
Was	der		

Marie: (1)______________ ist dein Beruf?

Max: Ich bin (2)______________ bei der Post. Und du? Was (3)______________ du?

Marie: Ich (4)______________ in einem Büro. *(office)*. Ich bin (5)______________. Was ist (6)______________ Beruf von Herrn Sehlers?

Max: Er ist (7)______________ in einem Krankenhaus. Was (8)______________ der Beruf von Frau Müller?

Marie: Sie ist (9)______________ in einem Hotel in Wien.

Max: Oh! Mein Pate hat auch eine (10)______________ in Wien.

E ***Zum Sprechen.*** **Working in pairs, you and your partner first make a list of 10 clues. Each clue should correspond to one of the occupations you have learned about in this unit. Then take turns telling one another the clues and guessing the associated occupations. If either one of you cannot correctly identify an occupation and its definite article on the first try, keep on guessing. If you'd like to compete against your partner, assign one point per correct article and one point per correct word. The winner is the first one to earn the most points.**

Beispiele:
A: orchestra
B: der Musiker
A: Ja!

A: tractor
B: die Köchin
A: Nein!

Name: ______________________________ Datum: ____________________

F **Complete these sentences. The clues to help you are in the last three words in each sentence. These words tell you the location or where the person works. Look very closely at these words and see if you can figure them out. *Viel Glück!***

1. Ich arbeite auf dem Lande. Ich bin ______________________________.
2. Ich arbeite in einem Orchester. Ich bin ______________________________.
3. Ich arbeite in einer Küche. Ich bin ______________________________.
4. Ich arbeite in einem Postamt (bei der Post). Ich bin ______________________________.
5. Ich arbeite in einem Theater. Ich bin ______________________________.
6. Ich arbeite in einem Krankenhaus. Ich bin ______________________________.
7. Ich arbeite in einem Büro. Ich bin ______________________________.

G **Choose an occupation from the list in your textbook. Pretend that you have this job and write in German what your occupation is, and where you work. (See exercise F as a model.) Then write as much as you can about your occupation.**

____

____

____

____

____

____

____

____

____

____

____

____

____

Name: ______________________________ Datum: ______________________

H Kreuzworträtsel

Waagerecht

1. installs lighting fixtures (female)
6. _____ *ist dein Beruf?*
8. *Ich arbeite* _____. (I enjoy working.)
11. runs a business (male)
13. saws wood (male)
14. diagnoses an illness (female)

Senkrecht

1. teaches a class (female)
2. occupations
3. cares for sick people (male)
7. place where a *Schauspieler* works
9. *Was* _____ *du?*
10. manages a farm (male)
12. *Erst die* _____, *dann das Vernügnen.*

Name: ______________________ Datum: ______________________

Look at the ad and the two business cards. Answer the questions.

Ad

1. This company wants to have young people apply for jobs. Find the words that mean "modern jobs for young people."

   ____

   ____

2. The first "A" word means job training. Write it down.

   ____

3. What kind of place is an *Arbeitsplatz?*

   ____

4. What kind of work would a *Landmaschinenmechaniker* do?

   ____

   ____

5. How many different job areas within the company are there? (Hint: Look near the *BayWa* logo. *Auf Deutsch, bitte.*)

   ____

Business Cards

Tierklinik Dr. Gaal
Von-Imhof-Straße 5 · 94419 Reisbach
Telefon 0 87 34 / 76 76 · Fax 0 87 34 / 9 31 25

Kleintiersprechstunde nach tel. Terminvereinbarung
Mo. - Fr. 9^{00} – 11^{00} und 15^{00} – 18^{00}
Sa. 9^{00} – 11^{00} und nach Absprache
NOTFÄLLE jederzeit

Ulrike Retzer
Rechtsanwältin
§
Moosfürther Straße 64
94522 Wallersdorf
Telefon: 0 99 33 / 95 18 20
Telefax: 0 99 33 / 95 18 21
retzer@retzer-wallersdorf.de

6. What kind of doctor is Dr. Gaal?

   ____

7. Who are his patients?

   ____

8. The lawyer's last name is Retzer. What is her *Vorname*?

   ____

9. Where does the lawyer have her office?

   ____

Name: ______________________ Datum: ______________

UNIT 9

A Select the letter of the item that corresponds to each situation.

_____ 1. You are thirsty.

A. Kekse B. Käse C. Messer D. Saft

_____ 2. You are hungry.

A. Mineralwasser B. Salz C. Brot D. Serviette

_____ 3. You want to eat fruit.

A. Hähnchen B. Birne C. Tasse D. Bohnen

_____ 4. You are going to have some soup and need a utensil.

A. Löffel B. Vase C. Gabel D. Serviette

_____ 5. You want some dessert.

A. Spinat B. Wurst C. Eis D. Milch

B You are having guests for a special dinner this evening. Create a menu. *(Auf Deutsch, bitte.)*

1. Appetizer: Crackers and ______________________
2. Main dish or specialty: ______________________
3. Three vegetables: ______________________

____

4. Dessert: ______________________
5. Two beverages: ______________________

____

Name: ______________________________ Datum: ______________________

C Match each item with its description.

_____	1. seasoning for meat or vegetables	A. Zucker
_____	2. bread spread	B. Tasse
_____	3. container to hold milk or juice	C. Glas
_____	4. sweetener	D. Mittagessen
_____	5. cutting utensil	E. Löffel
_____	6. container for coffee or tea	F. Salz
_____	7. first meal of the day	G. Frühstück
_____	8. utensil for eating soup	H. Messer
_____	9. table covering	I. Butter
_____	10. mid-day meal	J. Tischdecke

D Specialties. Circle the letter of each correct answer.

1. What are *Königsberger Klopse?*

   A. steaks B. ham sandwiches C. meatballs

2. What is a *Hühnerfrikassee?*

   A. a main dish B. a dessert C. a beverage

3. What are some ingredients in a *Strammer Max?*

   A. honey and spices B. ham and eggs C. carrots and peas

4. What is *Schweinebraten?*

   A. meat lasagna B. roast pork C. chicken potpie

5. How are *Spätzle* made?

   A. by dropping a flour and egg mixture into boiling water B. by stir frying flour and eggs in a lightly greased skillet C. by forming a loaf and baking it about an hour

6. What is the main ingredient in *Linseneintopf?*

   A. lentil beans B. roast chicken C. fried potatoes

7. Which city is known for the *Allerlei* vegetable dish?

   A. Königsberg B. Nürnberg C. Leipzig

8. What is a *Stollen?*

   A. a cake with a cream filling B. a loaf of holiday bread C. a dish of mixed vegetables

9. How is *Lebkuchen* sometimes prepared?

   A. as a bittersweet bar B. as a soft-centered candy C. as a heart-shaped cookie

10. Which fruits are in an *Erdbeertorte?*

    A. strawberries B. cherries C. blueberries

E **Word Search *(Buchstabensalat)*. Find and circle the German equivalent for each of the 14 English words listed. All the words appear in this unit. Remember that words may go forward, backward, up, down, or diagonally.**

```
I R T W D O Y U O X Z B L G L A S L
I M T I S C H G Q V S P G F W S I M
Z B T W G X F Q O T H K X S T I S R
E S S E N A H D P X R D S O F C K B
V M X E U R B T X U Q E L I H F L S
H Z V J R S B E D D R L N W S N A M
W M D B R D Y S L V E B E H Y J A M
X H U W R R B Y I N L I S S K H U K
G X M U B O P E T P N G G R L P T Y
K S P C E I T B E E S O U Z Y A I A
N V B N T T K U B R U G E E K X Z R
I B M Z E D U R S T T I N E S U C E
P B W H H M A Q I Q T O Q D E H L H
S B K G R T D J A E G E R H O Z I U
H X M F E U S W N K W L C T T F J N
A T E N V S N W A B U L I Ä E X C G
Z D K P W C F I G X I J P C V P R E
A G E L M A F H Y M K S X H Y Q Z R
```

1. food
2. holiday bread
3. roast pork
4. milk
5. napkin
6. meals
7. hunger (Are you "hungry"?)
8. strawberry cake
9. noodle dish
10. glass
11. table
12. fork
13. bread
14. thirst (Are you "thirsty"?)

Name: ______________________ Datum: ______________

F **Set the table by drawing on it all the items below. Make sure you have a nice *Bleistift* with an eraser. You are the *Künstler* now. After you draw an item, check the name off the list. If you run out of space on your table, don't worry. Try to draw as many items as you can. Neatness counts, so take your time and make an attractive table.**

Check list	Check
eine Tischdecke	_____
ein Teller	_____
eine Gabel	_____
ein Messer	_____
ein Löffel	_____
ein Teelöffel	_____
eine Serviette	_____
eine Vase	_____
eine Tasse	_____
eine Untertasse	_____
ein Glas	_____
Butter	_____
Pfeffer	_____
Salz	_____

G ***Zum Sprechen.* Draw or find pictures of flatware (eating utensils) and the foods and beverages of this unit. Show each picture to your partner, asking what it is. He/she will answer in German. If the answer is incorrect, you must correct the error. When your partner has completed all the pictures, change roles. Now, you answer each question. (Be sure to include the correct indefinite article, *ein* or *eine*, with the noun.)**

Beispiele:

You: Was ist das? *(showing picture of a glass)*
Your partner: Das ist ein Glas.
Your partner: Was ist das? *(showing picture of a spoon)*
You: Das ist eine Gabel.
Your partner: Nein. Das ist ein Löffel.

Name: ______________________ Datum: ______________________

H *Zum Sprechen.* **Your friend invites you to his/her house for a snack. Ask in German what there is to eat. Your friend will give you a choice of three fruits, cookies, or ice cream. Say "*Good. I am hungry! Thank you.*" Then select one of the items (such as an apple), and say "*An apple, please!*" In German, of course!**

I **Look at the two ads and the recipe. Answer all the questions *auf Deutsch*.**

Brot und Kuchen täglich frisch!

***Doppelback-Schnitten* ads**

1. Name two freshly baked items that the grocery store features.

____

2. Find a word that means twice or double baked.

____

3. The bread slices are sold by weight: How much does 500 grams cost?

____

4. What do you see next to the bread?

____

Name: ______________________________ Datum: ____________________

Feiner Aprikosenkuchen

Zutaten für 12 Stücke:
125 g Butter, 250 g Mehl, 150 g Zucker, 2 Päck. Vanillin-Zucker, 1 Prise Salz, 500 g Aprikosen, 250 g Schmand oder saure Sahne, 3 Eier, 500 g Vanilleeis.

ZUBEREITUNG:
Fett in Stückchen, Mehl, 75 g Zucker, 1 Päckchen Vanillin-Zucker und Salz verkneten. Zugedeckt ca. 30 Min. kühl stellen. Aprikosen heiß überbrühen und die Haut abziehen. Die Aprikosen halbieren, entsteinen. Schmand, 75 g Zucker, 1 Päck. Vanillin-Zucker und Eier verrühren. Mürbeteig auf bemehlter Arbeitsfläche rund (ca. 32 cm Ø) ausrollen. Tarteform mit herausnehmbarem Boden (28 cm Ø) fetten und mit dem Teig auslegen. Teig am Rand etwas hochdrücken. Aprikosen auf dem Teig verteilen. Schmandguss darüber gießen. Im vorgeheizten Backofen auf der unteren Schiene (E-Herd: 175 °C/Gas: Stufe 2) ca. 1 Std. backen. Tarte in der Form ca. 30 Min. abkühlen lassen. Dann herausnehmen und auskühlen lassen. Dazu schmeckt Vanille-Eiscreme.

Zubereitungszeit 1¾ Std. Pro Stück 1210 kJ/290 kcal.
E 5 g; F 15 g; KH 33 g Preis pro Stück: 0,40 Euro

Dessert recipe

5. What is this dessert? *(Auf Deutsch und Englisch, bitte.)*

____

6. What kind of food is an *Aprikose?*

____

7. For how many pieces of this cake is this recipe?

____

8. What ice cream goes especially well with this dessert? *(Auf Deutsch und Englisch, bitte.)*

____

Name: ______________________________ Datum: ____________________

UNIT 10

A Complete each sentence by writing the name of the appropriate artist.

1. If you like bold outlines and colors, you might like some of the paintings by ____________.
2. If you like fine detail in a picture, you might enjoy artwork by ____________.
3. If you like contemporary and unusual style, you might like the works of the contemporary artists ____________, ____________, and ____________.
4. If you like a bit of fantasy, you might enjoy the works by ____________.
5. If you appreciate art and the environment, you might like the sculptures by ____________.

B Find the painter(s) associated with each term. Write the name(s) in the space provided. Choose from:

Dürer | Rauch and Weischer | Kirchner and Marc | Friedrich

1. Romanticism: ____________________
2. New Leipzig School: ____________________
3. Expressionism: ____________________
4. Classicism: ____________________

Name: ______________________________ Datum: ____________________

C ***Wer?* Make sure you have read about the famous artists. Identify each of the following. Who . . .**

1. studied art in Dresden? ____________________
2. was the artist from Nürnberg? ____________________
3. worked in München? ____________________
4. came from Greifswald? ____________________
5. is a contemporary sculptor? ____________________
6. is a contemporary etcher and engraver? ____________________
7. is a contemporary painter? ____________________

D ***Ich bin Künstler!* This is the place where you get to be an artist. Don't worry if you are not artistic. Perhaps you are more of an abstract painter than a conventional painter! See if you know your German words well enough to draw each item listed below. Have fun!**

1. ein Kuli
2. ein Computer
3. ein Zelt
4. eine Hütte
5. ein Hund
6. eine Gabel
7. ein Löffel
8. ein Messer

Name: ______________________ Datum: ______________________

Now draw a picture to show what each sentence means. (Stick figures are fine!)

1. Stefan liest ein Buch.

2. Anja spricht mit dem Briefträger.

3. Benjamin streichelt die Katze.

4. Es gibt fünf Teller auf dem *(on the)* Tisch.

Name: ______________________ Datum: ______________________

F Look at the clippings and then answer the questions.

Kunstwerke für die Ewigkeit

Kunstobjekte

Meisterwerke der Uhrmacherkunst

Höhepunkte der Buchkunst

Zeitlos schöne Gartenkunst

Perlen der Schmuckkunst

Name: ______________________________ Datum: ______________

1. Find the German word for "artwork."

____

2. Find the German word for "art objects."

____

3. What kind of art does the word *Buchkunst* suggest?

____

4. What kind of art does the word *Uhrmacherkunst* suggest?

____

5. What kind of art does the word *Schmuckkunst* suggest?

____

6. What kind of art does the word *Gartenkunst* suggest?

____

Name: ______________________________ Datum: ____________________

G **Word Search (*Buchstabensalat*). Find and circle the 12 words or names found in this unit. You'll have to come up with the German equivalent for each English word listed. Remember that words and names may go forward, backward, up, down, or diagonally.**

Q V R K I R C H N E R M X Q K K A

F U Z D Z P D U K V B U Q U G T K

N R P F N M W R I Q X R D X S F E

L V O M M Z E G E B T C Z O R M D

Z C J S T L R X Q I E H U E G W Z

C B U R E E E M F L O J H B B D D

R S K T T M B B I D M C B Z Q A K

E L T H X S Y K Y K S N K K O Ü D

A O C N A G R O V I F R E Z N J J

V I K M A R C D E R D Z Q S D J M

R G B U N Y L W I N P I T T C X V

W F F K N O L E V M B L C E C P P

O K W E J S D O Q E E R U W I K K

S U S G L R T L V R A L W Q N D G

F K P F I I I F C U Y O F D F H A

M Z M C N Z T L C K B C R E R Ü D

I O H N U Z D H T G J L X H A S T

1. art
2. Richter
3. Marc
4. artist
5. Rauch
6. Friedrich
7. Dietz
8. Weischer
9. Dürer
10. Votteler
11. Kirchner
12. picture

H ***Du bist dran!*** **Of the all the artwork presented in this unit, decide which one is your favorite. Your teacher will designate a corner or a spot in your classroom for a discussion of each picture. Go to the area where your favorite picture will be discussed. Find out why everyone likes this picture the best. Write down the reasons. Choose a spokesperson to report your reasons to the entire class. Listen to what all the groups have to say and write down the survey results. What can you say about the artistic tastes of your class?**

Name: ______________________ Datum: ______________

UNIT 11

A Match the English with the German.

_____	1. hair	A. der Fuß
_____	2. nose	B. das Ohr
_____	3. foot	C. das Knie
_____	4. chest	D. der Kopf
_____	5. neck	E. die Nase
_____	6. elbow	F. die Brust
_____	7. ear	G. der Hals
_____	8. eye	H. der Ellenbogen
_____	9. knee	I. das Haar
_____	10. head	J. das Auge

B Odd one out! Circle the letter of the body part that does not belong with the expression.

1. Geh an die Tafel!

   A. der Fuß B. der Ellenbogen

2. Schreib!

   A. die Hand B. das Kinn

3. Lies!

   A. die Stirn B. die Augen

4. Hör zu!

   A. die Brust B. das Ohr

5. Sprich!

   A. die Zehe B. der Mund

Name: ______________________________ Datum: ______________

C Ergänze die fehlenden Buchstaben! *(Write the missing letter in each word.)*

1. die __chulter
2. der A__m
3. der Hal__
4. das Kni__
5. der __und
6. das Gesic__t
7. die S__irn
8. der Ba__ch
9. das __ein
10. das Ha__r

D *Die Körperteile* (Parts of the Body). Answer each question with a word in German.

1. What tells you that something is baking in the oven? ______________
2. What needs calcium to make them strong? ______________
3. What do you open at dinnertime? ______________
4. What do you use to throw a ball? ______________
5. What do you use to play the piano? ______________
6. What should you protect from loud noises? ______________
7. What has a cornea and an iris? ______________
8. What part of your body stores your brain? ______________

Name: ______________________ Datum: ______________

E **Ergänze die Sätze auf Deutsch!** ***(Complete the sentences in German with the words for the appropriate body parts.)***

zwischen = between	*Mitte* = middle	*über* = above

1. Die ______________ ist zwischen dem Hals und dem Bauch.
2. Der ______________ ist zwischen den Schultern.
3. Der ______________ ist zwischen der Schulter und der Hand.
4. Das ______________ ist in der Mitte des Beines.
5. Der ______________ ist in der Mitte des Körpers.
6. Die ______________ ist in der Mitte des Gesichts.
7. Die ______________ ist über den Augen.
8. In dem ______________ sind die Nase, die Augen und der Mund.
9. Die Hand hat fünf ______________.
10. Es gibt zweiunddreißig ______________ in dem Mund.

F **Word box. Arrange the words and sentences under the two columns: Positive and Negative.**

Positive: for words that convey *positive* feelings of health and happiness
Negative: for words that convey *negative* feelings of illness and unhappiness

die Gesundheit
Ich bin traurig.
Ich bin glücklich.
Kopfweh
krank
Es geht mir schlecht.
gesund
Es geht mir gut.

Positive ☺	**Negative** ☹
______________	______________
______________	______________
______________	______________
______________	______________

Name: ______________________________ Datum: ______________

G Ergänze die Sätze auf Deutsch. *(Complete the sentences in German.)*

1. JÜRGEN: Ich bin krank.

   EVELYN: Was hast ____________? *(What's wrong?)*

   JÜRGEN: Ich habe ____________. *(headache)*

2. LEA: Es geht mir schlecht.

   BETTINA: Was ____________ du? *(What's wrong?)*

   LEA: Ich habe die ____________. *(flu)*

3. MAHMOOD: Wie geht's?

   FELICIA: Es ____________ mir gut. *(I'm fine.)*

4. HELMUT: Wie fühlst du dich?

   CHRISTL: Ich ____________ mich schlecht.

5. SEPP: Bist du krank?

   ERICH: Nein! Ich bin ____________.

H Schreib auf Deutsch!

1. I'm feeling fine. ____________
2. I'm feeling awful. ____________
3. I'm happy. ____________
4. I'm sad. ____________

Name: ______________________ Datum: ______________

I ***Zum Sprechen.*** **Working in pairs, practice the German names for the parts of the face and parts of the body. You will need a doll, a teddy bear, or photographs of yourselves. Take turns pointing to a part, asking what it is and whether it is a part of the face or part of the body. The other one should answer.**

Beispiel:
A. Was ist das?
B. Das ist eine Schulter.

A. Ist das ein Gesichtsteil oder ein Körperteil?
B. Das ist ein Körperteil.

J ***Zum Sprechen.*** **In the space provided draw a person, one section at a time. Working in pairs, your partner announces a part of the body, for example, *der Fuß*, and you draw it. Continue until the picture is completed. You might try drawing a cat or another animal, but you may have to look up some German words, such as tail, paw, etc.**

Name: ______________________ Datum: ______________________

K Kreuzworträtsel

Waagerecht

1. where the headache is
5. happy
6. sick, ill
10. *Jürgen _____ die Grippe.*
11. health
13. needed to chew food, plural

Senkrecht

1. needed to kneel
2. needed to use the keyboard, plural
3. *Ich _____ mich schlecht.*
4. needed to see, plural
7. body
8. *Es _____ mir gut.*
9. _____ *fühlst du dich?*
12. needed to smell

Name: ______________________ Datum: ______________

L **Look at the clippings and then answer the questions.**

***Kopf*: a product is being advertised to relieve the symptoms of your cold.**

1. Find the German word that describes how your head feels.

____

2. Find the German word that describes how your nose is.

____

3. Do you sometimes *husten* (cough) when you have a cold? *(Auf Deutsch, bitte.)*

____

4. I wish you a *Gute Besserung*. What does that mean?

____

Name: ______________________ Datum: ______________________

Greenpeace Stickers

5. *Unser Leben* means "our life." Find two things that are "our life." *(Auf Deutsch, bitte.)*

____

6. Which word means "water"?

____

7. Which word means "forest"?

____

8. Because of exhaust fumes and pollution, people are urged to keep their cars out of the city (and take public transportation instead). Find the words that say: We must stay outside.

____

Name: ______________________ Datum: ______________

UNIT 12

A Match the English description with the German article of clothing.

_____	1. dressy female attire	A. die Bluse
_____	2. formal male attire	B. der Mantel
_____	3. bedtime or casual attire	C. der Bademantel
_____	4. worn around the neck	D. die Mütze
_____	5. female attire with a skirt	E. der Anzug
_____	6. (sports) cap	F. die Jacke
_____	7. covering for the head	G. der Hut
_____	8. short jacket	H. die Krawatte
_____	9. overcoat or long coat	I. der Gürtel
_____	10. worn to hold up trousers	J. das Kleid

B Odd one out! Circle the letter of the item that does not belong with the others.

1.	A. die Handschuhe	B. der Mantel	C. der Schlafanzug
2.	A. die Baseball-Mütze	B. die Bluse	C. der Hut
3.	A. das Taschentuch	B. der Gürtel	C. die Moden
4.	A. das Kleid	B. das Hemd	C. die Krawatte
5.	A. das Hemd	B. die Bluse	C. die Socken

Name: ______________________________ Datum: ____________________

C Name the article of clothing that you wear or use in the following situations. *Auf Deutsch, bitte.*

1. You wear this over your pajamas. ______________________
2. You put these on your hands. ______________________
3. You use this when you blow your nose. ______________________
4. You use this to secure your skirt or pants. ______________________
5. You wear this on your head. ______________________
6. You wear these on your feet. ______________________

D What's the price? Finish each sentence with the German word for each item in parentheses.

1. Wie viel kostet die ______________________? *(blouse)*
2. Wie viel kostet der ______________________? *(suit)*
3. Wie viel kostet die ______________________? *(cardigan sweater)*
4. Wie viel kosten die ______________________? *(shoes)*
5. Wie viel kosten die ______________________? *(socks)*

Name: ______________________________ Datum: ____________________

E **Find your way through the clothing store. Name the articles of clothing that you encounter on the way.**

____

____

____

____

____

____

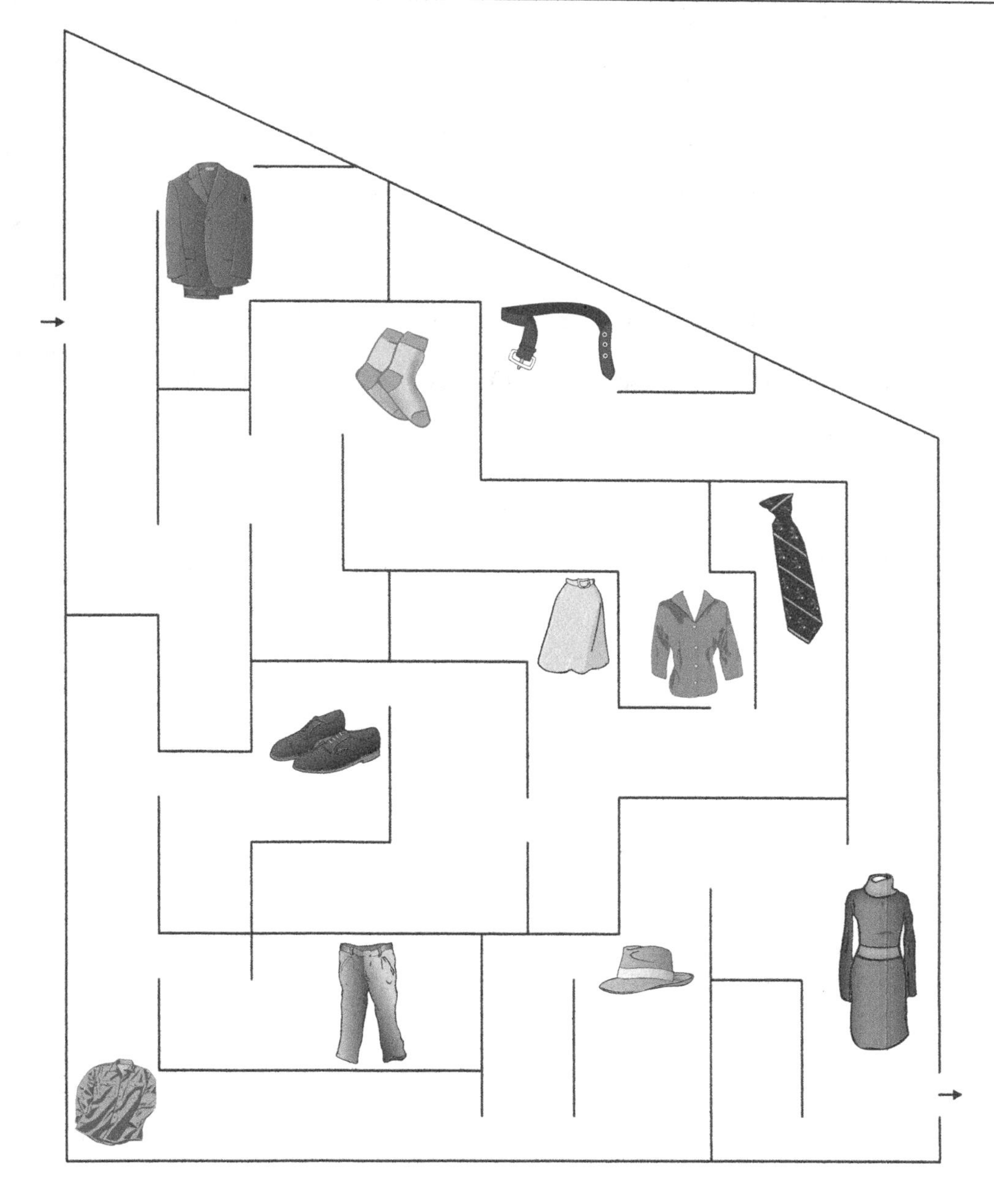

Name: ______________________________ Datum: ______________________

Word Search *(Buchstabensalat)*. Find and circle the German equivalent for each of the 10 English words listed. Remember that words may go forward, backward, up, down, or diagonally.

V Z Y E X U T H K Z C M J Q I
W S S O C K E N Z H G A Y G O
V L E T N A M T S I C F Q F D
H Q O E F A E I S K S T N Y U
J Q D Y C S V G E Y Q M J S O
P U L L I S W E H U H C S D V
M Q T E W E H E F V L Q R T U
G U O L J C S N E S U L B G U
A N R B T O W X E L T K T J Z
G B C F H Q B C M Ü T Z E D K
K J X E U B C J Y V R V N X T
T W D U L G T W O O K D F L M
C A N E D M E H A J B Z B Y V
B I V I S L J G T R O C K F M
Z H V I I H S H F O F T O L U

1. jacket
2. pullovers (short form)
3. socks
4. coat
5. shoes
6. swimming trunks
7. skirt
8. shirts
9. cap
10. blouses

Name: ____________________ Datum: ____________________

Zum Sprechen. **Who wears what and where? Begin by thinking in German of five occupations. (See Unit 8.)**

Step 1: **As you say the name of each occupation, your partner will say one item of clothing typically worn by that person. You keep track of how many of your partner's answers are correct. Once a mistake is made, there is no second chance. He/she loses a point.**

Beispiel:	You say:	*Tischler*
	Your partner:	*Schuhe.* Appropriate/Correct, one point for partner. If he/she answered *Rock,* that would be incorrect. No point.

Step 2: **Then your partner says five articles of clothing. You must respond with a place where one might wear each item.**

Beipiel:	Your partner:	*Krawatte*
	You answer:	Formal dinner. Correct, one point for you.

The winner is the player with more points than the other player within a designated time frame.

Name: ______________________ Datum: ______________________

H **Complete the dialogues. Select the words from the word box. You will not use all the words listed.**

Dialogue 1

Konzert	Schlafanzug	Anzug

GERD: Was hast du an?

KLAUS: Ich habe meinen neuen ______________ an.

BERND: Warum?

KLAUS: Ich gehe heute Abend in ein ______________.

Dialogue 2

Garten	Krawatte	Jacke

REBECCA: Was hast du an, Katrina?

KATRINA: Eine ______________.

REBECCA: Warum?

KATRINA: Ich gehe in den ______________.

Dialogue 3

Badezimmer	Hut	Bademantel

ALEX: Was hast du an, Georg?

GEORG: Meinen ______________.

ALEX: Warum?

GEORG: Ich gehe gleich in das ______________.

Dialogue 4

schön	gesund

HEIKE: Wie ist das Hemd?

HANNELORE: Das Hemd ist ______________.

Dialogue 5

glücklich	klein

FRANZ: Wie sind die Schuhe?

ANNELIESE: Die Schuhe sind mir zu *(too)* ______________.

Name: ______________________ Datum: ______________________

I Look at both ads and then answer the questions.

1. The prices shown take effect after a certain date. Do you know when?

   ____

2. Find the German word for quilted jackets.

   ____

3. The word *sportlich* describes the appearance of these jackets. How would you express this term in English?

   ____

4. The word *leger* refers to their weight. Guess what this one means!

   ____

5. The word *Tasche* (pocket) appears twice. Find those instances and write them down.

   ____

6. A *Handy* is a cell phone. Name a place indicated where you can put it.

   ____

Name: ______________________ Datum: ______________

7. What is the word for “sizes”?

____

8. *Wie viel kostet eine Steppjacke?*

____

Name: ______________________ Datum: ______________

UNIT 13

A Answer each question by selecting the appropriate letter.

_____ 1. At what time does the sun rise?

A. um sechs Uhr zwei

B. um zwei Uhr sechs

_____ 2. At what time does the sun set?

A. um ein Uhr

B. um neunzehn Uhr

_____ 3. At what time do you leave for school in the morning?

A. um dreizehn Uhr

B. um halb acht

_____ 4. At what time are you dismissed from school every day?

A. um fünfzehn Uhr

B. um Mitternacht

_____ 5. What time is good for star-gazing?

A. fünfzehn Uhr

B. dreiundzwanzig Uhr

Name: ______________________ Datum: ______________________

B Wie viel Uhr ist es? *(Use numbers and colons to express each time.)*

Beispiel: Es ist halb neun. = 8:30

1. Es ist Viertel vor zehn. ____________
2. Es ist halb vier. ____________
3. Es ist zwanzig Uhr. ____________
4. Es ist siebzehn Minuten nach fünf. ____________
5. Es ist ein Uhr. ____________
6. Es ist Viertel vor acht. ____________
7. Es ist zehn Minuten vor zwölf. ____________
8. Es ist zwanzig nach vier. ____________
9. Es ist Mitternacht. ____________
10. Es ist Mittag. ____________

C The 24-hour clock system. For each time at the left, state it in regular time.

Beispiel: 14 Uhr = 2 P.M.
21 Uhr 30 = 9:30 P.M.

1. 13 Uhr: ______________________
2. 22 Uhr: ______________________
3. 17 Uhr 40: ______________________
4. 23 Uhr 51: ______________________
5. 18 Uhr 25: ______________________

Name: ______________________ Datum: ______________

D **Identify the color generally associated with each item.** ***(Auf Deutsch, bitte.)***

1. strawberries: ______________________
2. rain clouds: ______________________
3. snowflakes: ______________________
4. sunflowers: ______________________
5. crows: ______________________
6. sky on a nice day: ______________________
7. pumpkins: ______________________
8. tree trunks: ______________________
9. moss and ferns: ______________________
10. lilacs: ______________________

E **Color Combinations. Each color at the left is a combination of two others. Write the German names.**

1. grün = ______________________
2. orange = ______________________
3. grau = ______________________
4. rosa = ______________________
5. violett = ______________________

Name: ______________________ Datum: ______________________

F Kreuzworträtsel

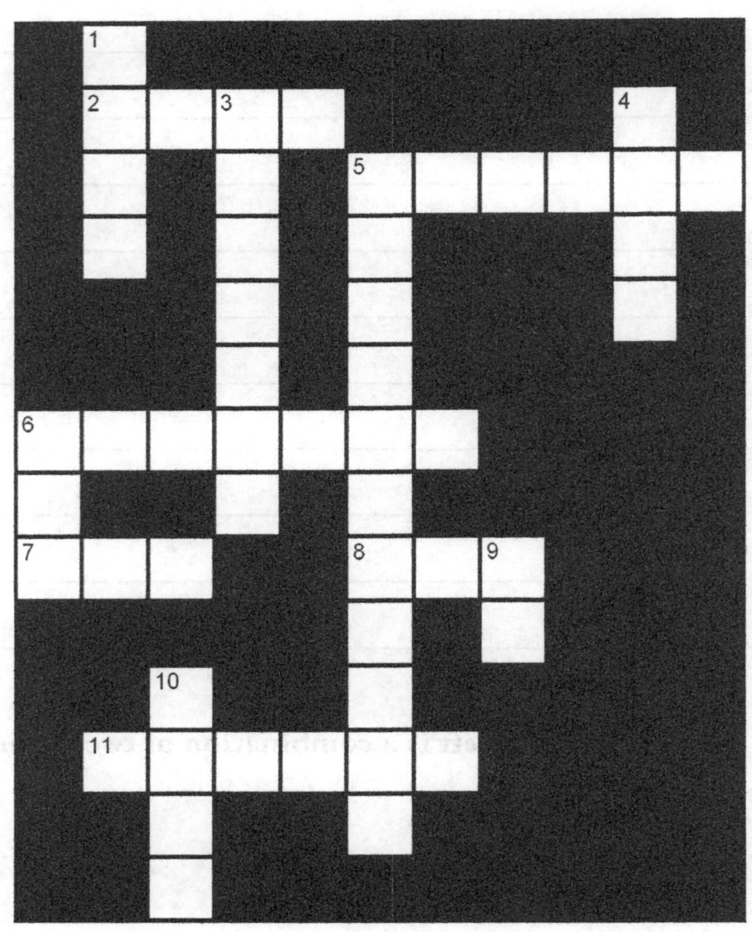

Waagerecht

2. combination of red and white
5. when the sun is at its highest point in the sky
6. quarter
7. color of a stop sign
8. *Besser spät als _____.*
11. _____ *Farbe hat das Gras?*

Senkrecht

1. combination of white and black
3. color of pepper
4. after
5. between 11:59 P.M. and 12:01 A.M.
6. before
9. _____ *ist ein Uhr.*
10. color of butter

Name: __________ Datum: __________

G ***Zum Sprechen.*** **At what time do you do certain things? Make up a list of ten activities you do on a regular basis. Then find a partner and work in pairs. Your partner chooses one activity from your list and asks you at what time you do that activity. You answer in German.**

> **Beispiel:** A: At what time do you generally eat supper?
> B: Um sechs Uhr.

H ***Zum Sprechen.*** **Working in pairs, take turns identifying the colors around you. Your partner must find objects of different colors. He/she says "*I see something in this room that is . . .*" (and mentions a color in German). You are to identify that object in German, if you can.**

I **Look at the two ads and then answer the questions.**

Uhr

1. What is unusual about the clock?

   ____

2. According to this clock: *Wie viel Uhr ist es?*

   ____

3. What does *Viertel vor* mean?

   ____

4. How much time is the *Zeitspanne*?

   ____

5. What time on the 24-hour clock is equivalent to 5 P.M.?

   ____

Name: ______________________ Datum: ______________________

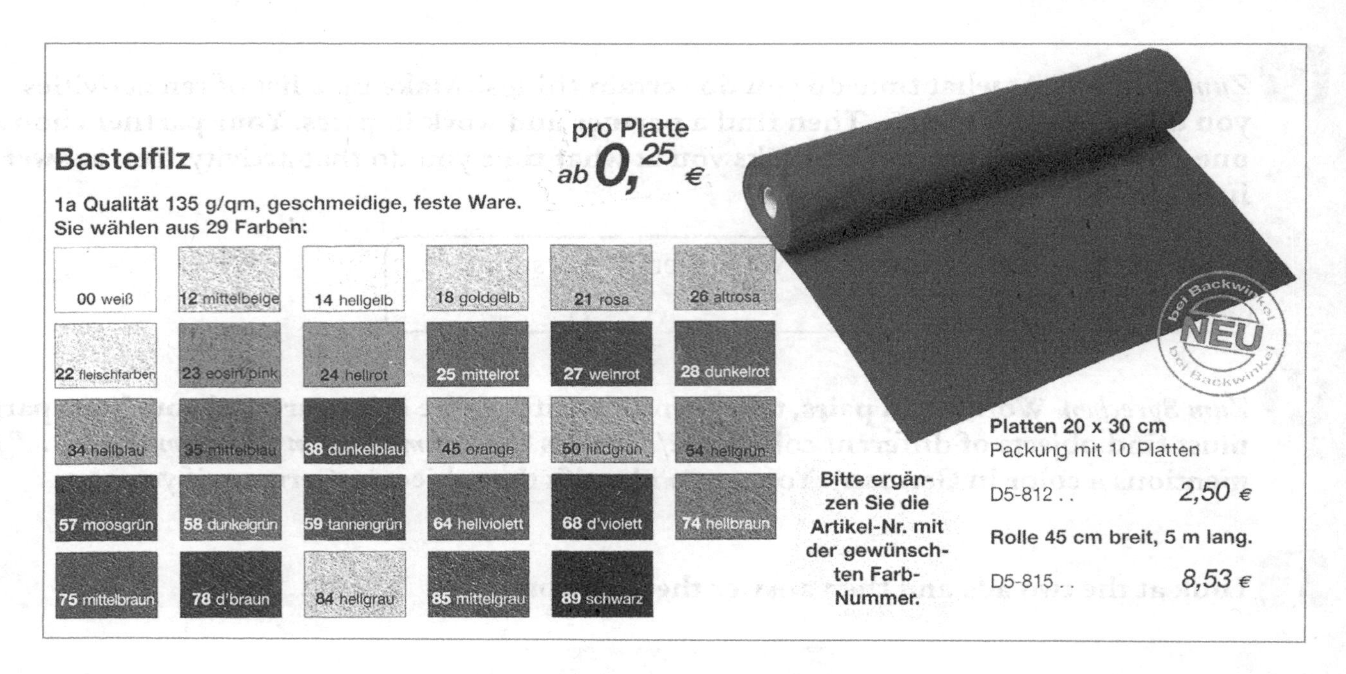

Bastelfilz

6. What color is *mittelbraun*?

____

7. What color is *dunkelblau*?

____

8. What color is *hellgelb*?

____

Name: ______________________ Datum: ______________

UNIT 14

A Identify each work of music by name.

1. choral work named after a saint: ______________
2. opera named after a musical instrument: ______________
3. concertos named after a place in Germany: ______________
4. symphony associated with nature: ______________
5. symphony associated with a Roman god: ______________

B Name a musician associated with each place.

1. Leipzig: ______________
2. Salzburg: ______________
3. Bonn: ______________
4. Eisenach: ______________
5. Vienna: ______________

C Select the letter of the correct answer.

_____ 1. Who as a child entertained kings and queens?

A. Beethoven

B. Bach

C. Mozart

_____ 2. Who taught youngsters how to sing?

A. Mozart

B. Bach

C. Beethoven

_____ 3. Who was interested in equality and freedom?

A. Beethoven

B. Mozart

C. Bach

_____ 4. Who wrote works called cantatas and fugues?

A. Beethoven

B. Mozart

C. Bach

_____ 5. What amazed Mozart's audiences?

A. his ability to sing at different ranges

B. his ability to build and repair keyboards and harpsichords

C. his ability to reproduce musical works from memory

_____ 6. Who is considered the finest example of the Romantic style of music?

A. Beethoven

B. Bach

C. Mozart

_____ 7. Who wrote 41 symphonies?

A. Bach

B. Mozart

C. Beethoven

_____ 8. Who became deaf?

A. Beethoven

B. Mozart

C. Bach

_____ 9. Who was poorly paid?

A. Beethoven

B. Bach

C. Mozart

_____ 10. Who became blind?

A. Mozart

B. Beethoven

C. Bach

D Unscramble the composers' first names *(Vornamen)*.

1. GWLUDI ______________________
2. NONJAH ______________________
3. GFALOWNG ______________________
4. SIBNEASTA ______________________
5. MAUDASE ______________________

E Match the German name of a musical instrument with its corresponding description. You should have little difficulty figuring these out.

_____ 1. die Klarinette

_____ 2. die Geige

_____ 3. die Trompete

_____ 4. die Orgel

_____ 5. die Trommel

_____ 6. die Flöte

_____ 7. die Gitarre

A. This instrument has pipes, a console, and pedals.

B. This instrument is long and straight.

C. This instrument is beaten with sticks.

D. This instrument is held alongside the musician's face.

E. This instrument is played with a bow.

F. This instrument plays *reveille*, a camp wake-up call.

G. This instrument is a favorite of country-western and rock singers.

Name: ______________________ Datum: ______________

F Contemporary Music: Match the singers with the descriptions.

_____	1. Thomas Quasthoff	A.	well known songwriter and performer
_____	2. *Wir sind Helden* and *Juli*	B.	popular singer of a rock band
_____	3. Xavier Naidoo	C.	recent bands
_____	4. *Clepsydra*	D.	singer of classical music
_____	5. *Die Dissidenten*	E.	group promoting world harmony
_____	6. Herbert Grönemeyer	F.	band from Switzerland

G Interview your partner about musical preferences. Ask him/her the following questions and note the answers. Then reverse roles so that your partner interviews you. Compare and contrast your results.

1. What is your favorite type of music?

____

2. What is the name of your favorite group or singer?

____

3. Do you (or did you ever) play an instrument? ________ If so, which one(s)?

____

4. Do you (or did you ever) join a band or orchestra?

____

5. Do you (or did you ever) participate in chorus?

____

6. Who are your favorite female and male singers?

____

7. What is the name of a favorite song?

____

8. What do you like better in a song: the melody or the rhythm?

____

Name: ____________________ Datum: ____________

9. Do you (or did you ever) take dance lessons?

____

10. Did you ever do a waltz, rumba, tango, cha cha, foxtrot, swing, polka, or folk dance?

____

11. What is the name of a dance that you like?

____

12. Who is one of your favorite composers?

____

13. What is the name of one of your favorite musical works?

____

14. Did you ever see a stage production such as a musical or an opera?

____

15. Did you ever attend a concert of rock music?

____

16. Did you ever attend a concert of classical music?

____

Name: ______________________ Datum: ______________________

H Look at the concert ticket and schedule and then answer the questions.

Donnerstag, 3. August
BRIXEN Konzert mit der Gruppe **„Quarrymen“** am Domplatz – Beginn: 20.30 Uhr
Mit freundlicher Unterstützung der Firma barth

Freitag, 4. August
ST. ANDRÄ Konzert der **Musikkapelle** auf dem Festplatz
Beginn: 20.30 Uhr

Samstag, 5. August
BRIXEN Konzert des **„Sibley High School String Orchestra“** am Domplatz – Beginn: 20.30 Uhr
Mit freundlicher Unterstützung der Firma serima

TILS Konzert der **Musikkapelle „Peter Mayr“ Pfeffersberg** im Vereinshaus
Beginn: 20.30 Uhr

Dienstag, 8. August
BRIXEN Orgelkonzert mit **Luca Scandali** im Dom zu Brixen - Beginn: 20.30 Uhr (Musik & Kirche)

Donnerstag, 10. August
BRIXEN Konzertante Freilichtaufführung der Operette „Die Lustige Witwe“ auf dem Domplatz
Ausführende: **Haydnorchester von Bozen und Trient** und **Solisten Gabriele Fontana** und **Peter Weber** – Leitung: Peter Guth
Beginn: 21.00 Uhr – Eintritt: Lit. 15.000
Mit freundlicher Unterstützung der Stadtverwaltung Brixen

Freitag, 11. August
AFERS Konzert der **Musikkapelle Afers** auf dem Festplatz – Beginn um 20.30 Uhr

1. Find the German word for entrance.

____

2. Who lived here?

____

3. Where is it?

____

4. How much does the ticket cost?

____

5. What do you think the number 68236 represents?

____

6. Where will the Sibley High School String Orchestra be performing?

____

7. Who is giving an organ recital?

____

8. *Um wie viel Uhr beginnt das Konzert in Afers?*

____

Name: ______________________ Datum: ______________________

UNIT 15

A Match the German with the English.

_____	1. Es schneit.	A. sun
_____	2. Wie ist das Wetter?	B. What's the season?
_____	3. der Frühling	C. It's sunny.
_____	4. kalt	D. It's snowing.
_____	5. schlecht	E. wind
_____	6. die Sonne	F. bad
_____	7. der Wind	G. cold
_____	8. Welche Jahreszeit haben wir?	H. spring
_____	9. Es blitzt.	I. It's/There's lightning.
_____	10. Es ist sonnig.	J. How's the weather?

Name: ______________________ Datum: ______________

B Explain your reasons in German for advising someone what to pack or do.

1. Take warm clothing because:

   Im Winter ist es in Berlin ______________.

2. Take lightweight clothing because:

   Im Sommer ist es in München ______________.

3. Take a hat and coat because:

   Im Herbst ist es in Wien ______________ *und* ______________.

4. Take an umbrella because:

   Im Frühling ______________ *es oft in Deutschland.*

5. Take a ski outfit because:

   Im Winter ______________ *es viel in Österreich.*

6. Take sunscreen because:

   Im Sommer ist es ______________ *in Europa.*

7. When there is an electrical storm, stay inside because:

   ______________________________.

C Welche Jahreszeit haben wir? *(Name in German the season when the following weather is typical.)*

1. Es ist schön. ______________
2. Es ist windig und es regnet. ______________
3. Es schneit. ______________
4. Es ist windig und kühl. ______________
5. Es ist schwül. ______________

Name: ______________________ Datum: ______________

D **Name the season when the following events usually take place.** ***Auf Deutsch, bitte.***

1. Many birds fly south. ______________________
2. Some animals hibernate. ______________________
3. It feels better to be in the shade than in the sun. ______________________
4. The air gets warmer and the snow starts to melt. ______________________
5. You make jack-o'-lanterns out of pumpkins. ______________________
6. Trees begin to make buds. ______________________

E **Write a sentence in German that describes the weather associated with each clue.**

1. lawn chair:

   ____

2. ice skates:

   ____

3. lilacs and violets:

   ____

4. snowsuit:

   ____

5. leaf rake:

   ____

6. perspiration:

   ____

7. electricity in the sky:

   ____

8. noise in the sky:

   ____

Name: ______________________ Datum: ______________________

F **Find your way through the seasons. Using the pictures as clues, name the weather conditions you encounter on your way.**

______________________ ______________________

______________________ ______________________

______________________ ______________________

______________________ ______________________

______________________ ______________________

______________________ ______________________

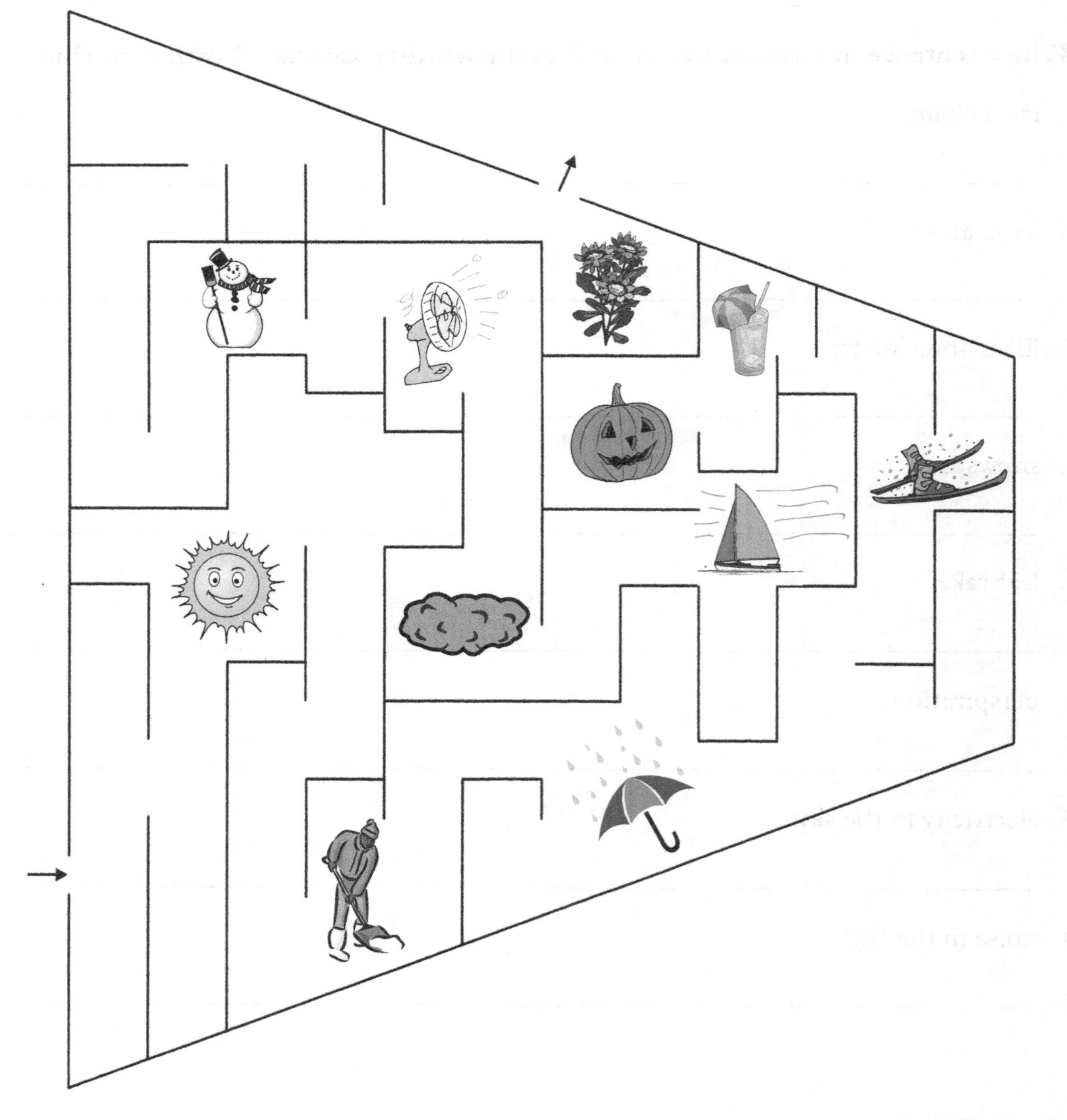

Name: ______________________ Datum: ______________________

G ***Zum Sprechen.* Make a list of German sentences that describe the weather. Then, working in pairs, say each sentence as a cue for your partner. He/she will say the related season and a related item (clothing or accessory).**

> **Beispiel:** A. Es ist sonnig.
> B. Sommer; Sonnenbrille *(or)* Wir haben Sommer./Ich trage meine Sonnenbrille.

H **Word Search *(Buchstabensalat)*. Find and circle the German equivalent for each of the 12 English words listed. Remember that words may go forward, backward, up, down, or diagonally.**

G	Z	D	G	Q	Q	M	L	Ü	W	H	C	S	C	F	K
V	H	P	O	C	L	X	Y	C	P	Q	V	M	J	U	C
G	S	O	M	M	E	R	B	L	H	Ü	K	Z	B	W	L
N	C	B	B	Z	D	K	F	F	G	L	L	H	X	V	R
I	W	O	L	K	I	G	D	H	W	E	T	T	E	R	Z
L	N	Z	K	B	L	Z	Y	N	R	W	Q	R	C	K	W
H	L	B	A	L	T	H	B	V	I	M	H	E	T	K	E
Ü	X	Z	M	N	T	D	K	C	B	W	L	B	L	S	J
R	O	Q	R	U	S	I	D	I	R	L	N	M	T	U	A
F	S	G	T	S	B	R	E	H	R	M	T	C	L	W	H
O	N	I	I	L	C	Z	B	Y	W	A	R	M	K	I	Y
X	F	Z	E	N	A	L	G	C	X	Z	A	A	G	N	K
T	K	L	B	Z	N	M	H	E	A	S	L	A	F	T	R
N	F	Q	S	W	M	O	Q	X	W	T	K	R	Q	E	U
I	I	B	M	X	N	B	S	F	A	L	M	Z	X	R	N
R	V	X	K	W	Y	C	U	S	K	L	H	J	T	Q	I

1. cool
2. wind
3. spring
4. sunny
5. cloudy
6. summer
7. warm
8. winter
9. humid
10. weather
11. fall, autumn
12. cold

Name: ______________________ Datum: ______________

I **Look at the weather report and then answer the questions.**

UNSER WETTER: SCHAUER ODER GEWITTER

EUROPÄISCHE STÄDTE

	gestern, 14 Uhr	heute, max.	morgen, max.
ATHEN	freundlich35°	sonnig 33°	sonnig 34°
BARCELONA	bedeckt 27°	freundlich29°	Schauer 27°
BOZEN	freundlich28°	Gewitter 23°	wechselh.26°
BRÜSSEL	wechselh.20°	wechselh.24°	wechselh.26°
BUDAPEST	freundlich30°	wechselh.33°	Gewitter 24°
FLORENZ	wechselh.34°	freundlich34°	Gewitter 31°
HELSINKI	bedeckt 15°	freundlich22°	wechselh.21°
INNSBRUCK	wechselh.25°	Gewitter 22°	Gewitter 18°
ISTANBUL	wechselh.29°	wechselh.32°	sonnig 32°
LAS PALMAS	freundlich25°	freundlich25°	wechselh.23°
LISSABON	freundlich22°	sonnig 25°	sonnig 25°
LONDON	freundlich22°	freundlich23°	sonnig 25°
MADRID	freundlich31°	freundlich33°	sonnig 34°
MOSKAU	freundlich29°	Schauer 25°	wechselh.24°
NIZZA	wechselh.28°	freundlich27°	sonnig 26°
OSLO	wechselh.16°	freundlich23°	sonnig 23°
PARIS	wechselh.24°	freundlich26°	wechselh.25°
PRAG	Regen 18°	Schauer 24°	Schauer 19°
ROM	freundlich32°	sonnig 33°	sonnig 32°
STOCKHOLM	bedeckt 17°	freundlich23°	sonnig 21°
VENEDIG	wechselh.31°	Gewitter 34°	sonnig 31°
WIEN	wechselh.27°	Schauer 27°	Schauer 20°
ZÜRICH	wechselh.23°	Gewitter 23°	Schauer 22°

1. The word *Schauer* sounds like its English counterpart. What does it mean?

   ____

2. *Gewitter* can be combinations of *Regen, Donner,* and *Blitz.* What are *Gewitter*?

   ____

3. *Das Wetter heute in Oslo ist freundlich.* Does that call for a *Regenschirm*?

   ____

4. *Gibt es heute gutes Wetter in Prag?*

   ____

5. *Was ist die Höchsttemperatur (max.) heute in Istanbul?*

   ____

6. *Scheint die Sonne heute in Zürich?*

   ____

7. *Wie ist das Wetter heute in Athen?*

   ____

8. *Regnet es heute in Moskau?*

   ____

Name: ______________________ Datum: ______________

UNIT 16

A Match the English with the German.

_____	1. birthday	A. Schultag
_____	2. today	B. Woche
_____	3. week	C. morgen
_____	4. day	D. Monat
_____	5. month	E. Geburtstag
_____	6. school day	F. Mittwoch
_____	7. tomorrow	G. Feiertag
_____	8. weekend	H. heute
_____	9. holiday	I. Wochenende
_____	10. Wednesday	J. Tag

B Rearrange the days of the week according to the German calendar.

Dienstag Sonntag Montag
Samstag Donnerstag Freitag Mittwoch

1. ______________________
2. ______________________
3. ______________________
4. ______________________
5. ______________________
6. ______________________
7. ______________________

Name: ______________________ Datum: ______________________

C Complete each sentence with a German word.

1. If today is *Mittwoch*, tomorrow is ______________.
2. If *gestern* was Saturday, ______________ is Monday.
3. If this month is *Dezember,* next month is ______________.
4. If the day before yesterday was *Donnerstag,* today is ______________.
5. If next month is *Oktober,* this month is ______________.

D Schreib auf Deutsch! *(Write the following dates in German. Follow the model.)*

Beispiel: Monday, February 27
Montag, der 27. Februar

1. Saturday, June 6: ______________
2. Wednesday, October 13: ______________
3. Sunday, December 19: ______________
4. Friday, May 21: ______________
5. Tuesday, August 7: ______________

E Schreib auf Deutsch! *(Write in German the day or month as indicated by the clue.)*

1. the day and month when people play jokes on each other: ______________
2. the day and month of U.S. Independence Day: ______________
3. the month when people send valentines: ______________
4. the day honoring the Norse goddess of love: ______________
5. the day honoring the god of war: ______________
6. the month of German Unity Day: ______________
7. the month in which Mother's Day occurs: ______________
8. the month in which Father's Day occurs: ______________
9. the day in honor of the moon: ______________
10. the day in honor of the sun: ______________

Name: ______________________________ Datum: ______________________

F **Read the questions and then choose the correct answers.**

_____ 1. Wann ist der Feiertag?

A. der Schultag B. übermorgen

_____ 2. An welchem Tag ist die Deutscharbeit?

A. am Mittwoch B. die Woche

_____ 3. Was hast du heute?

A. Montag B. eine Klavierstunde

_____ 4. Wann hast du Geburtstag?

A. übermorgen B. dreizehn

_____ 5. Was ist das Datum heute?

A. der erste November B. November

G ***Zum Sprechen.* You probably know the classroom activity called "Birthday Lineup." Now you can do this in German. In this activity all students will line up in the chronological order of their dates of birth. Begin by asking one classmate when his/her birthday is:**

Beispiel: A: Wann hast du Geburtstag?
B: Am 18. März.

Then depending on when your birthday is, stand to the right or left of this person. You will need to ask each classmate his/her date of birth in order to know if you should stand in line to the left or right. (Left side of person means that your birthday comes before his/hers; right side of person means that your birthday is after his/hers.) When all students are lined up in the correct birthday order, each one will say, in turn, his/her date of birth. In this way the entire class can check the accuracy of the lineup.

You might like to time this entire activity!

Beispiele:	Johnny	Gail	Tim	Joshua
	Am 2. April.	Am 29. April.	Am 15. Mai	Am 23. Juni.

H **Odd one out! Circle the word in each group that is unlike the others.**

1. Juni, November, Sonnabend
2. Dienstag, Januar, Mittwoch
3. Geburtstag, Samstag, Freitag
4. Montag, Feiertag, Sonntag
5. Woche, Monat, Dezember
6. Tag, Datum, Wochenende

Name: ______________________ Datum: ______________

I Look at the clippings and then answer the questions.

Ab 8. Juni im Handel!

ÖFFENTLICHER EISLAUF
(Ende April bis Anfang Juli geschlossen)

Montag - Sonntag	14.00 - 15.50 Uhr
Montag Discolauf	20.00 - 21.30 Uhr
ab Mitte September	19.30 - 21.00 Uhr

ab Mitte Oktober jeden Donnerstag um 20.15 Uhr
Eisstockschießen für Jedermann

Termine für Schlägerlauf und Eishockey-Spiele
entnehmen Sie bitte der örtlichen Presse

Tel. 0 83 62 / 50 75-10 · Fax 0 83 62 / 50 75-12
info@blz.fuessen.de · www.blz.fuessen.de

1. The word *gültig* means "valid." Will the specially reduced price for these products be available on the weekend?

   ____

2. The word *ab* refers to a date and means "as of" or "starting from." When will this product be on the market?

   ____

3. The Olympic-sized ice rink is open for public skating. Find the word for "ice skating."

   ____

4. When is it closed *(geschlossen)*? ______________________________

5. Is the rink open every day of the week during the open months? ______________

6. On what day can you skate to music? ______________________________

7. What are the additional skating hours as of the middle of September?

   ____

8. On what day of the week can you practice the sport of curling *(Eisstockschießen)*?

   ____

Name: ______________________ Datum: ______________

Unit 17

A

Identify the authors of each work by choosing a name from this list: Sarah Kirsch, Christa Wolf, Else Lasker-Schüler, Johann Wolfgang von Goethe, Friedrich Schiller, and E.T.A. Hoffmann.

1. *Die Panther-Frau:* ______________________
2. *Faust:* ______________________
3. *Maria Stuart:* ______________________
4. *Der geteilte Himmel:* ______________________
5. *Der siebente Tag:* ______________________
6. *Der Nussknacker und der Mausekönig:* ______________________

B

A literary work may be a novel, a story, a play (comedy or tragedy), a screenplay, a poem (lyric, epic, or dramatic), an essay, etc. It may be also a collection of poetry or stories. Can you identify each work below? What type of literature is each one?

1. *Faust:* ______________________
2. *Wilhelm Tell:* ______________________
3. *Hebräische Balladen:* ______________________
4. *Nussknacker und Mausekönig:* ______________________
5. *Landaufenthalt:* ______________________

C

Match the conflicts with the names of the literary works.

_____ 1. imagination versus reality

_____ 2. fulfillment versus loss

_____ 3. love versus politics

_____ 4. knowledge versus religion

_____ 5. love of country versus love of son

A. *Hebräische Balladen*

B. *Der geteilte Himmel*

C. *Faust*

D. *Wilhelm Tell*

E. *Nussknacker und Mausekönig*

Name: ______________________ Datum: ______________

D Write the name of the author that fits each description.

1. She was also a translator. ______________________
2. He was also a statesman. ______________________
3. He was also a musician. ______________________
4. She was also an artist. ______________________
5. He was also a physician. ______________________

E Name the city or geographical area associated with each author. Note that one location is used twice.

Frankfurt | Marbach | Berlin | Königsberg

German Democratic Republic (official name of East Germany)

1. Else Lasker-Schüler: ______________________
2. Johann Wolfgang von Goethe: ______________________
3. Sarah Kirsch: ______________________
4. Christa Wolf: ______________________
5. Ernst Theodor Amadeus Hoffmann: ______________________
6. Friedrich Schiller: ______________________

F What kind *(genre)* of books do you like to read? Decide if you prefer mysteries, adventure stories, science fiction, or other kinds of novels. Your teacher will designate a corner or another spot in your classroom as a discussion area for a particular *genre*. Go to the place that represents your favorite kind of books. Pair up with a partner. Each of you tells the other: (1) why you like these books, (2) the name of the last book of this kind you read, (3) the author, and (4) a brief description of the plot. Then join the other students in your corner and make a list of all your favorite titles. Put this list on the bulletin board and be sure to label its *genre*.

Look at all the lists. What can you say about the reading preferences of your entire class?

Name: ______________________________ Datum: ______________________

G Kreuzworträtsel

Waagerecht

4. writer who was also a statesman and theater director
6. first name of Classical author
7. genre of *Der geteilte Himmel*
9. genre of *Faust*
11. first name of Expresionist poet and artist

Senkrecht

1. genre of *Hebräische Balladen*
2. writer who was also a musician
3. poet who learned Russian
5. novelist born in Landsberg
6. *Ode to* _____, poem by Schiller and part of Beethoven's Symphony #9
8. first name of author who influenced Poe and Baudelaire
10. _____ *A sagt, muss auch B sagen.*

Name: ______________________ Datum: ______________

H **Look at the two ads and then answer the questions.**

19. Jahrgang

Buxtehuder
Bücher-Igel

Bücher für Mädchen und Jungen
von 10 bis 16 Jahren

Die Top 10 der Bücher

Familie&Co präsentiert in jeder Ausgabe die bei Amazon.de meistbestellten deutschsprachigen Kinder- und Jugendbücher

1 Dietrich H. W. Grönemeyer: Der kleine Medicus. Rowohlt, 22,90 Euro, Hardcover

2 Christopher Paolini: Eragon – Der Auftrag des Ältesten. Cbj, 19,90 Euro, Hardcover

3 J.K. Rowling: Harry Potter und der Halbblutprinz. Carlsen, 22,50 Euro, Hardcover

4 Morton Rhue: Die Welle. Ravensburger, 5,95 Euro, Taschenbuch

5 Hans de Beer: Der kleine Eisbär und der Angsthase. Findling, 2,95 Euro, Hardcover

6 Cornelia Funke: Tintenblut. Dressler/Nord-Süd-Verlag, 22,90 Euro, Hardcover

7 Gudrun Pausewang: Die Wolke. Ravensburger, 5,95 Euro, Taschenbuch

8 Paul Maar: Der Buchstaben-Fresser. Oetinger, 6,50 Euro, Hardcover

9 Cornelia Funke: Tintenherz. Dressler/Nord-Süd-Verlag, 19,90 Euro, Hardcover

10 Otfried Preußler: Der Räuber Hotzenplotz. Thienemann, 9,90 Euro, Hardcover

Buxtehuder Bookstore

1. What does the word *Igel* (hedgehog) help identify?

____

____

2. What age group of readers would enjoy the books in this bookstore?

____

____

3. What is the plural form of *das Buch*?

____

Die Top 10 der Bücher

4. The author who appears twice in this list is also well known in the U.S. Who is she?

____

5. Find the book title that is also a weather-related word. Who is the author?

____

6. *Der kleine Medicus* is an entertaining book that teaches children and adults about the workings of the human body. Who is the author?

____

7. *Wie viel kostet "Harry Potter und der Halbblutprinz"?*

____

8. Find the word for paperback (non hardcover).

____

Name: ______________________ Datum: ______________

UNIT 18

A Match the German with the English.

_____	1. das Rad	A. to dance
_____	2. das Spiel	B. beach
_____	3. reiten	C. to ski
_____	4. der Fußball	D. bike
_____	5. tanzen	E. to read
_____	6. der Strand	F. museum
_____	7. lesen	G. soccer
_____	8. schwimmen	H. game
_____	9. Ski laufen	I. to horseback ride
_____	10. das Museum	J. to swim

B Select a statement from the box to match the word clues.

Ich gehe zum Fußballspiel. Ich gehe auf die Party.
Ich gehe zum Strand. Ich gehe ins Museum.

1. Balloons, music, and noisemakers:

____

2. Soccer ball:

____

3. Paintings, sculptures, and exhibits:

____

4. Sand bucket, shovel, and seashells:

____

Name: ______________________________ Datum: ______________________

C Ergänze jeden Satz! *(Complete each sentence with a word from the box.)*

tanze	los	mitkommen	Rad	Baseball	klar

1. Ich spiele ______________________.
2. Ich fahre gern ______________________.
3. Was ist da ______________________?
4. Na, ______________________.
5. Willst du ______________________?
6. Ich ______________________ gern.

D Select the letter of the best answer to each question.

_____ 1. Wohin gehst du heute Abend?

A. Ich lese gern.

B. Ich spiele heute Basketball.

C. Ich gehe zum Fußballsspiel.

_____ 2. Wohin gehst du?

A. Auf die Party.

B. Na klar.

C. Am Samstag.

_____ 3. Welche Sportart treibst du?

A. Am Strand.

B. Volleyball.

C. Ja, gern.

_____ 4. Wo machen wir morgen ein Picknick?

A. Um drei Uhr.

B. Am Strand.

C. Am Sonntag.

_____ 5. Willst du mitkommen?

A. Ja.

B. Heute Abend.

C. Mit Timo.

_____ 6. Gehst du ins Museum?

A. Das Museum ist da drüben.

B. Das Museum heißt die *Alte Pinakothek*.

C. Ja. Das Dürerfest findet diese Woche statt.

Name: ______________________________ Datum: ____________________

E **Word Search (*Buchstabensalat*). Find and circle the German equivalent for each of the 12 English words listed. Words may go forward, backward, up, down, or diagonally.**

K P J S I W R O V T D V J L L K M

C V G J Y M C P F R Y V W A L O O

X F P A R A D F A H R E N B A P D

C D R C R G F O E R W X K A B H N

Z V H E Q Z J M W F T K X I Y G A

H I P C I Q D L I H N Y K L E V R

N P Q Z X Z N P E T H I L L L S T

E U N E T I E R D Y K A R O L B S

L U G K L A F I W K B O I B O O U

E N R T N C P C T S N J M Z V U F

I M R G E A V E S G F M B M A M O

P X M R S T S U T H Q Y L R E S T

S Z Z S E F F P I C K N I C K N D

Z J C P L I A U M U E S U M H M K

1. to bike
2. soccer
3. museum
4. picnic
5. to play
6. to come along
7. beach
8. to ride (on horseback)
9. volleyball
10. leisure time
11. party
12. to read

F **Schreib auf Deutsch!**

1. I'm going to the party tonight.

   ____

2. I'm going to the picnic tomorrow.

   ____

3. I'm going to the museum on Saturday.

   ____

4. I'm going to the beach on Sunday.

   ____

Name: ______________________ Datum: ______________________

G Welche Sportart treibst du? (Answer this question according to each set of clues.)

Beispiel: free kick, field goal, pass:
You write: *Ich spiele amerikanischen Fußball.*

1. strike, stolen base, inning: ______________________
2. spike, serve, net ball: ______________________
3. love, deuce, serve: ______________________
4. free throw, slam dunk, hoop: ______________________
5. goal, cleats, corner kick: ______________________

H *Zum Sprechen.* Interview five of your classmates to find out what they like to do in their free time. Ask each student the questions that follow and record each answer (*ja* or *nein*) in the space provided. Then summarize your findings.

(Do you like to . . .)	eins	zwei	drei	vier	fünf
1. Schwimmst du gern?	____	____	____	____	____
2. Tanzt du gern?	____	____	____	____	____
3. Liest du gern?	____	____	____	____	____
4. Läufst du gern Ski?	____	____	____	____	____
5. Spielst du gern Baseball?	____	____	____	____	____
6. Spielst du gern Fußball?	____	____	____	____	____
7. Fährst du gern Rad?	____	____	____	____	____
8. Gehst du gern ins Museum?	____	____	____	____	____
9. Spielst du gern ein Instrument?	____	____	____	____	____
10. Spielst du gern mit dem Computer?	____	____	____	____	____
11. Zeichnest du gern?	____	____	____	____	____
12. Sprichst du gern deutsch?	____	____	____	____	____

Name: ______________________ Datum: ______________________

Look at the article and the stamps. Answer the questions.

Briefmarken

Ein Hobby für Jung und Alt!

Starten Sie jetzt ein einzigartiges Sammelvergnügen!

Deutsche Briefmarken komplettieren sich zu einem ungewöhnlichen Bilderbuch der Erinnerungen, in dem sich auch Ihr eigenes Leben wiederfindet und an dem noch nachfolgende Generationen ihre Freude haben. Kinder und Kindeskinder werden es besonders zu schätzen wissen, wenn Sie ihnen diese Zeit fortlaufend dokumentieren.

1. What are *Briefmarken*?

   ____

2. Who might enjoy saving them and building a collection *(eine Sammlung)*?

   ____

3. The formal German word for "stamp collecting" starts with a *P*. Find it.

   ____

Name: ______________________________ Datum: ______________________

4. What kind of fun is meant by this word: *Sammelvergnügen*?

____

5. What is the value of the *Tulpe* stamp?

____

6. Is there a *Briefmarke* to encourage awareness of endangered *Vögel*?

____

7. Find the word for lighthouses.

____

8. Which *Briefmarke* encourages respect for others?

____

Name: ______________________________ Datum: ______________________

UNIT 19

A Which item in each group costs the most? Circle the letter of the item that generally is the most expensive. (How well do you remember the words from previous units?)

1.	A. ein Lineal	B. ein Mantel	C. drei Pfirsiche
2.	A. ein Heft	B. ein Glas Milch	C. eine Compact Disc
3.	A. ein Stuhl	B. fünf Tomaten	C. ein Kuli
4.	A. ein Bleistift	B. ein Hemd	C. ein Haus
5.	A. Tennisschuhe	B. eine Tasse Schokolade	C. ein Taschentuch
6.	A. ein Apfel	B. eine CD	C. grüne Bohnen
7.	A. ein Computer	B. ein Fußball	C. ein Anzug
8.	A. ein Zelt	B. eine Birne	C. fünfzig Pfirsiche
9.	A. eine Hütte	B. ein Mietshaus	C. ein Zelt
10.	A. vier Bananen	B. drei Schreibtische	C. zwei CDs

B Complete each sentence by changing the English word in parentheses to its corresponding German word.

1. (peaches) Ich kaufe acht ______________________.
2. (how much) ______________________ kostet diese CD?
3. (selection) Unsere ______________________ ist sehr groß.
4. (all) Das ist ______________________.
5. (change) Da ist Ihr ______________________.

Name: ____________________ Datum: ____________________

C **A customer asks about the price of several items. Play the part of the salesclerk as you answer each question. Make up prices that seem reasonable to you.**

Beispiele:	Wie viel kostet die Bluse? Die Bluse kostet 19,95 Euro.	Wie viel kosten die Kulis? Die Kulis kosten zwei Euro.

1. Wie viel kostet die Jacke? ____________________
2. Wie viel kosten die Kekse? ____________________
3. Wie viel kostet ein Basketball? ____________________
4. Wie viel kosten die Handschuhe? ____________________
5. Wie viel kostet eine Cola? ____________________

D **Circle the letter of the best answer to each question.**

1. Wohin gehst du?

   A. Die CD.

   B. Tennisschuhe.

   C. Zum Markt.

2. Wie viel kostet diese CD?

   A. Sie kostet 10 Euro.

   B. Ich möchte diese CD kaufen.

   C. Hier ist das Geld.

3. Noch etwas?

   A. Sie ist teuer.

   B. Hier ist Ihr Kleingeld.

   C. Ja, grüne Bohnen.

4. Was darf es sein?

   A. Ich gehe zum Einkaufszentrum.

   B. Ich möchte Tomaten kaufen.

   C. Es ist ein Kunde.

5. Was kaufst du?

   A. Schuhe.

   B. Reduzierter Preis.

   C. Verkäufer.

6. Kostet diese Hose 45 Euro?

   A. Ja, das ist ein reduzierter Preis.

   B. Hier ist das Geld.

   C. Danke schön

Name: ______________________________ Datum: ______________

E Complete these dialogues.

1. Was darf es sein?

   Ich möchte ein Buch ______________________.

2. Was kaufst du?

   Drei ______________________.

3. Ist die Schokolade teuer?

   Nein, sie ist sehr ______________________.

4. ______________________ gehst du?

   Ich gehe zum Einkaufszentrum.

5. Noch etwas?

   ______________________, zehn Pfirsiche, bitte.

F *Part 1:* The conversation that follows is between a salesclerk and a customer, but the sentences are all mixed up. Rearrange them by putting them in logical order, beginning with 1 for the first sentence in the dialogue, 2 for the second, etc. Number 1 is already marked for you.

__1__ Was darf es sein?

_____ Danke schön. Noch etwas?

_____ Wie viel kostet diese CD?

_____ Gut. Ich kaufe die CD. Hier ist das Geld.

_____ Sie kostet 29 Euro.

_____ Nein, das ist alles.

***Part 2:* Now, in the space below, copy all the sentences in their correct order.**

____

____

____

____

____

____

Name: ______________________ Datum: ______________________

G **Find your way through the store to the cash register. Name the items you encounter on your way.**

____

____

____

____

____

____

____

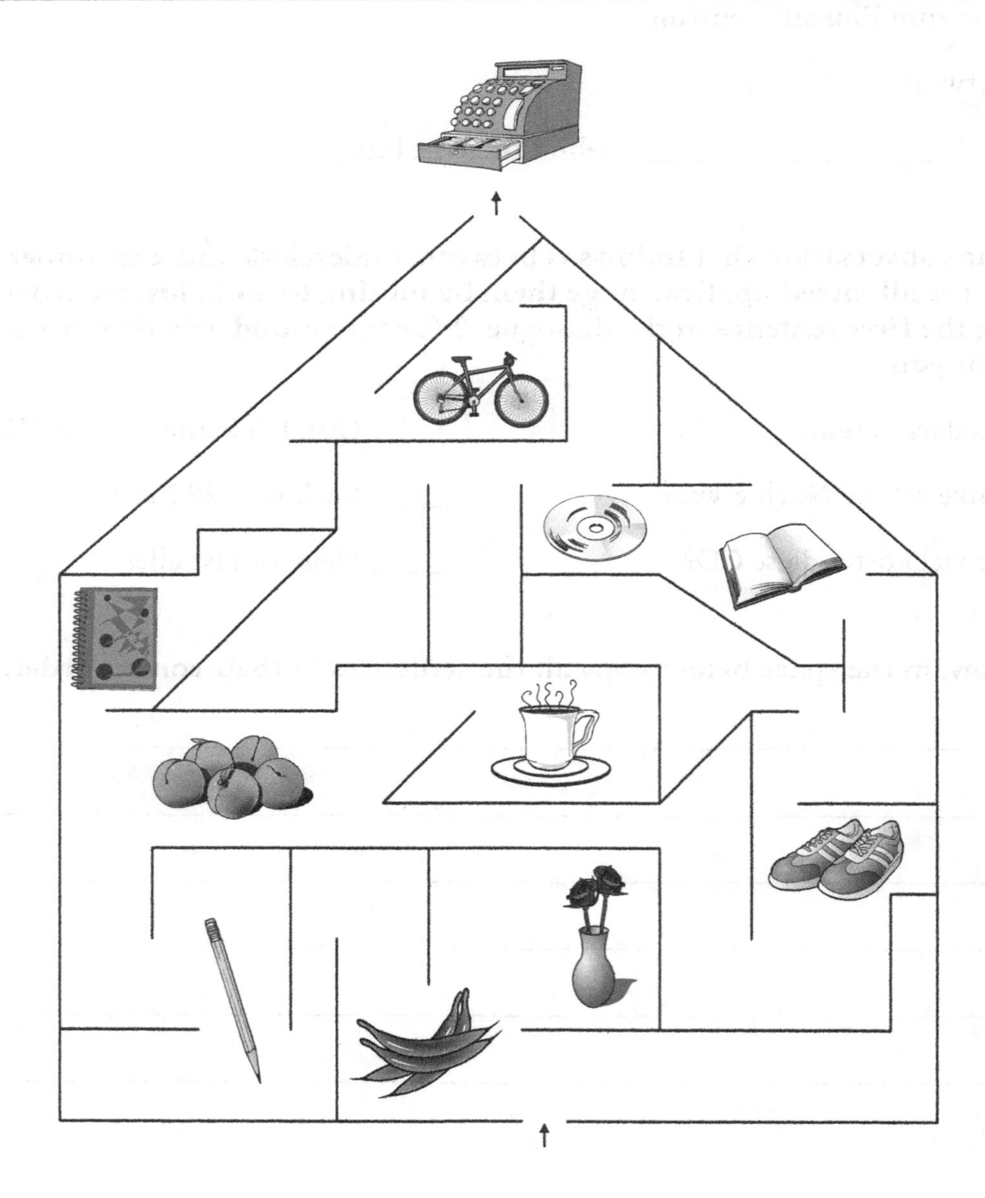

Name: ______________________ Datum: ______________________

H ***Zum Sprechen.*** **Imagine that you are at a shopping center. You and your partner play the roles of a salesclerk and a customer. Carry on a short conversation in German in which the customer makes a purchase. Limit your questions to those you have already practiced in class. Be sure to respond appropriately to your partner's questions and comments. In the course of the conversation:**

1. The clerk and the customer greet each other.
2. The clerk asks the customer if she wants some help.
3. The customer mentions a particular item and asks its price.
4. The clerk tells the price.
5. The customer says that she will buy it.
6. The clerk asks her if she wants anything else.
7. The customer says "That's all" and pays for the item.
8. The clerk thanks the customer and gives her the change.

Name: ______________________ Datum: ______________

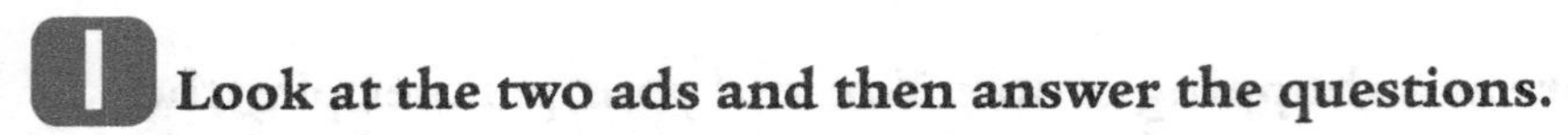

I **Look at the two ads and then answer the questions.**

1. What word suggests "top-notch technology"?

   ____

2. *Wie viel kostet der DVD-Rekorder?*

   ____

3. The set-up menu is supposed to be easy to figure out. What does *benutzerfreundlich* mean?

   ____

4. *Fettarme Milch* has no fat. What do these words mean?

   ____

5. This product comes in a one "L" container. What does "L" stand for?

   ____

6. *Wie viel kostet die Packung?*

   ____

7. The item pictured to the left of the milk carton: *Was ist das?*

   ____

8. On the milk carton: *Wie viele Kühe gibt es?*

   ____

Name: ______________________________ Datum: ____________________

UNIT 20

A Travel questions. Answer each one by choosing the right letter.

_____ 1. Who carries a suitcase?

A. ein Koffer   B. die Reisende   C. die Kundin

_____ 2. What tells you arrival and departure times?

A. ein Reisepass   B. eine Fahrkarte   C. der Fahrplan

_____ 3. What permits you to travel internationally?

A. ein Reisepass   B. ein Koffer   C. ein Flugsteig

_____ 4. How can you get to Vienna?

A. um Mitternacht   B. mit dem Auto   C. der Angestellte

_____ 5. Which words tell you where something is?

A. der nächste Zug   B. um neunzehn Uhr   C. rechts

B What is the missing word? Can you suggest a word to complete each statement?

1. Um wie viel Uhr fährt der ______________________ Zug nach Berlin?
2. Hier ist ______________________ Rückfahrkarte.
3. Steigen Sie am ______________________ aus.
4. Wie ______________________ ich zum Hotel Krone?
5. Am ______________________ 20.

Name: ______________________________ Datum: ______________________

C Find the best answer to every question.

_____ 1. Wo steht der Bus? A. Eine Fahrkarte.

_____ 2. Was kaufst du? B. Um vierzehn Uhr.

_____ 3. Wie heißt das Hotel? C. Im Koffer.

_____ 4. Um wie viel Uhr fährt der Bus? D. Auf der Straße.

_____ 5. Wo ist die Kleidung? E. Vier Jahreszeiten

D Give the German name for a vehicle associated with each word.

Part 1

1. der Flughafen: ______________________________
2. der Bahnhof: ______________________________
3. der Ozean: ______________________________
4. die Garage: ______________________________
5. die Straße: *(public transport)* ______________________________

Part 2

Now write that you travel by each of these vehicles.

1. ______________________________
2. ______________________________
3. ______________________________
4. ______________________________
5. ______________________________

Name: ______________________________ Datum: ____________________

E **Complete each sentence with a word from the box.**

Fahrkarte	Schalter	Bahnhof	Zug	Frankfurt

1. Ich fahre mit dem Taxi zum ____________________.
2. Ich reise um zwanzig Uhr zehn nach ____________________.
3. Ich gehe zum ____________________.
4. Ich kaufe dort eine ____________________.
5. Ich habe meinen Koffer. Wo steht der ____________________?

F ***Zum Sprechen.*** **Imagine that you are in a train station in a German-speaking country. You and your partner play the roles of a clerk at the ticket counter and a traveler. Carry on a short conversation in German in which the traveler buys a ticket. Limit your questions to those you have already practiced in class. Be sure to respond appropriately to your partner's questions and comments. In the course of your conversation:**

1. The clerk and the traveler greet each other.
2. The traveler tells the clerk what city he's going to and asks at what time the next train is leaving.
3. The clerk tells the traveler the time.
4. The traveler tells the clerk that he/she would like a round-trip ticket in second class and asks a price.
5. The clerk tells the traveler the price.
6. The traveler pays for the ticket.
7. The clerk thanks the traveler and gives him/her the change.

Name: ______________________ Datum: ______________

G Answer the questions based on the illustration and the ticket.

Der neue **Berliner Hauptbahnhof**

DB

Drehkreuz für internationale Züge
Der neue Berliner Hauptbahnhof ist ein Symbol für das zusammenwachsende Europa. Von hier aus sind die europäischen Metropolen mit dem Zug zu erreichen. Die Stadt wird zur Drehscheibe für den internationalen Verkehr. Dazu gehört, dass der Berliner Hauptbahnhof mit großen Bahnhöfen in europäischen Hauptstädten enge Kooperationen vereinbart hat.

1. The German Federal Railroad has an abbreviation. What is it?

   ____

2. What building is shown in the sketch?

   ____

3. What kind of vehicles would you expect to see here? *(Auf Deutsch, bitte.)*

   ____

4. In what city was this sightseeing ticket used?

   ____

5. For what kind of vehicle was the ticket used?

   ____

6. *Wie viele Personen* used this ticket?

   ____

7. What is the total price?

   ____